THE
WEIDER BODY
BOOK

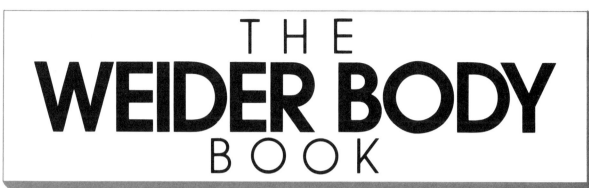

THE WEIDER BODY BOOK

BY BETTY WEIDER & JOE WEIDER

Contemporary Books, Inc.
Chicago

Library of Congress Cataloging in Publication Data

Weider, Betty.
   The Weider body book.

   Includes index
   1. Bodybuilding for women.   2. Exercise for
women.   3. Women--Nutrition.   I. Weider, Joe.
II. Title.   III. Title: Body book.
GV546.6.W64W435   1984   646.7′5   84-12724
ISBN 0-8092-5429-8

Exercises photographed by John Balik at Gold's Gym, Venice Ca. All other photo-
graphs courtesy of the IFBB.

Published by Contemporary Books, Inc.
180 North Michigan Avenue, Chicago, Illinois 60601
Manufactured in the United States of America
Library of Congress Catalog Card Number: 84-12724
International Standard Book Number: 0-8092-5429-8

Published simultaneously in Canada by Beaverbooks, Ltd.
195 Allstate Parkway, Valleywood Business Park
Markham, Ontario L3R 4T8 Canada

CONTENTS

1.	BODY BY WEIDER	1
2.	SUPERCHARGING YOUR WORKOUT	9
3.	WORLD-CLASS LEGS	23
4.	DIAMOND-SHAPED CALVES	41
5.	BREATHTAKING BACKS	53
6.	BLASTING THE BUSTLINE	73
7.	DYNAMIC DELTS	93
8.	ARMED TO WIN	111
9.	RIPPLING WAISTLINE	139
10.	ADVANCED TRAINING PRINCIPLES	154
11.	BODYBUILDING NUTRITION	167
12.	FINE TUNING	175
	INDEX	193

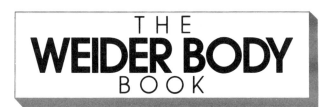

THE
WEIDER BODY
BOOK

Probably the hottest new star in bodybuilding is Lori Bowen who won the American and USA Championships in 1983 and the Pro World Championship in 1984.

1
BODY BY WEIDER

Bodybuilding is booming, both as a means of shaping and conditioning the body and as a competitive sport. Literally hundreds of thousands of women have adopted a bodybuilding lifestyle—training with weights and monitoring their diet—in the last couple of years. And from its humble beginnings as a competitive sport in 1979, bodybuilding has grown to become a viable international sport with more than a hundred high-level women's competitions held each year in the United States alone.

This book is a sequel to our popular *The Weider Book of Bodybuilding for Women* (Contemporary Books, 1981), and it's intended to take up where our initial women's bodybuilding training manual left off. So, don't expect to find any advice for beginning weight trainees and bodybuilders in *Body by Weider;* if you need that type of advice, you should first read *The Weider Book of Bodybuilding for Women.* In this volume we will give you in-depth advanced training advice that you can use to further improve your physical appearance, fitness, health, and sense of well-being. And if you are so inclined, you can use our advice to become a successful competitive bodybuilder.

So, *do* you want to become a competitive bodybuilder? It's certainly not an easy lifestyle to maintain, and to many the rewards are not readily apparent. But there are many rewards from competitive bodybuilding, over and above the trophies or prize money that you might win. Trophies just collect dust, and money seems to evaporate quite quickly in modern life, but the more intrinsic rewards stemming from bodybuilding last and benefit you for a lifetime.

Following are eight intrinsic rewards that you can expect from adopting a bodybuilding lifestyle:

1. *The ability to set and reach worthwhile goals.* Bodybuilding is the world's most diffi-

1

cult sport. Not only do bodybuilders train as hard as any other athletes; they often do so when their energy reserves have been depleted by strict precontest dieting. As a result, bodybuilders must be goal-oriented in order to succeed at their sport. And if you can successfully use the goal-setting process to improve your bodybuilding results, you can use goal-setting to improve any and all other areas of your life.

2. *Improved self-reliance.* Bodybuilding is not only a difficult sport but also a lonely sport. No one can do your workouts for you; you always have to do them yourself, relying only on your own initiative and abilities to succeed. As a result, bodybuilders are very self-reliant individuals who willingly succeed or fail totally on their own merits.

Transferring this quality to the rest of life liberates you from dependence on others.

3. *Increased self-discipline.* When you are confronted with a task as difficult as bodybuilding, it takes a great deal of self-discipline to succeed at the activity. And those who are successful bodybuilders have gradually learned how to discipline themselves. If you can discipline yourself to diet strictly for two or three months to compete successfully in a bodybuilding show—and get into the gym for a two-hour workout when you barely have the energy to brush your teeth—you can certainly muster enough self-discipline to sit down every night to study for your next day's classes or to get to work a couple of hours early to finish an important business report.

Rachel McLish, twice Ms. Olympia titleholder, has achieved all eight of the intrinsic rewards of bodybuilding.

4. *The ability to work hard.* In order to reach your goals in serious weight training and bodybuilding, you must work very hard, an ability that seems foreign to most nonbodybuilders. But the ability to work hard and in focus (i.e., to work toward a goal rather than in a random, undisciplined pattern) will make you a success in life. Furthermore, bodybuilding gives you an appreciation for the work ethic, because in bodybuilding you will see a direct relationship between how hard you work and what you get out of the sport. Simply put, the harder you work in the gym, the greater your results as a bodybuilder.

5. *Improved mental concentration.* Have you ever wondered why some people seem to work less at their jobs and still produce more high-quality work than others who seem constantly busy? The reason for this is usually that better workers have greater powers of concentration. Bodybuilders soon learn pinpoint concentration, or they wouldn't be successful, and this ability to concentrate transfers readily to the work arena and the remainder of life.

6. *Greater self-esteem.* When you do something well, and virtually any woman can easily see herself succeeding in serious weight training and bodybuilding, you will automatically feel better about yourself. Over the years, we have seen literally hundreds of timid women gradually become lionesses through weight training and bodybuilding. So if you feel timid and lack self-esteem, you can readily see an improvement in how you feel about yourself and react to those around you.

7. *Increased ability to do heavy work.* If nothing else, heavy weight training makes you very strong, allowing you to carry easily a heavy bag of groceries that might previously have nearly broken your back or to push a stalled car over to the side of a street. Reserve strength can also highly benefit you in potentially life-threatening situations. Several women bodybuilders have survived with flying colors auto accidents and muggings that could have injured or even killed them, simply because they were proportionately so strong. And that isn't such a bad by-product of bodybuilding training.

8. *Improved income.* Many women don't consider the fact that professional bodybuilders make a very good income from their sport, some bringing in more than six figures per year. Some of the opportunities for earning additional money available to women bodybuilders are outlined in the following section.

PRO BODYBUILDING

The number of female professional bodybuilders making a living from the sport is rapidly increasing. And with the correct marketing approach, to say nothing of being persistent, you probably have a 50-50 chance of becoming a pro bodybuilder if you stick with it long enough and work with 100 percent effort to reach your goals.

Following are nine of the best sources of income available to professional women bodybuilders:

1. *Prize money.* The prize money available in pro competitions has become significant during the three years between writing *The Weider Book of Bodybuilding for Women* and *The Weider Body Book.* It is not uncommon for first prize at a pro show to be $25,000 and sixth to be as high as $5,000. During the 1983 competitive season Carla Dunlap banked more than $50,000 in prize money alone. If you're near the top in competitive bodybuilding and you're willing to lay it on the line at every show, you can make some big money just competing.

2. *Posing exhibitions.* The amount of money a pro bodybuilder can make by guest-posing at various competitions has also risen dramatically in the last three years. The top women can now command up to $2,000–$2,500 per exhibition, and most good women bodybuilders now make at least $1,000 per guest-posing appearance. Champion women bodybuilders can often schedule more than 20 exhibitions per year, sometimes as many as eight to ten in one two-week tour of Europe or the Far East. We are sure that there are many top women body-

builders making more than $50,000 per year from exhibition fees.

3. *Training seminars.* Up-and-coming body-builders always want to know how the champions do it, so women who can express themselves well—or who can learn to do so—are able to give training seminars all over the world, making up to $2,000 per session. It's not uncommon for a high-level pro woman bodybuilder to schedule an exhibition and seminar virtually every weekend when not actively peaking for a competition.

4. *Personal coaching.* If you prefer one-on-one instruction and happen to live in a large metropolitan area, you can make a goodly amount of money by personally coaching aspiring bodybuilders. You will have spent hundreds of hours learning every facet of bodybuilding in order to reach the pro level, so you might as well get a return for your knowledge.

5. *Personal appearances.* Well-publicized women like Rachel McLish, Carla Dunlap, Candy Csencsits, and Shelley Gruwell are in demand for personal appearances at gym openings and other bodybuilding-oriented public functions. Fees vary widely for personal appearances, but in general they are comparable to what you can make at a training seminar.

6. *Mail order income.* The best female bodybuilders have thriving mail order businesses dependent on advertisements in *Muscle & Fitness*, *Flex*, and *Shape*. Up to $3,000 per week can be earned from selling through the mail such items as training courses, photos, T-shirts, posing suits, posters, and personalized instruction through cassette tapes.

7. *Product endorsements.* Promoters of training equipment, clothing, and food supplements often use champion bodybuilders to endorse their products. A casual glance at *Muscle & Fitness* ads for our products will convince you that we frequently use women bodybuilders, and we pay them well for their endorsements.

8. *Writing.* Several women bodybuilders

Shelley Gruwell is interviewed for an HBO telecast of the 1980 Miss Olympia contest.

have cashed in on the lucrative book publishing market by writing their own books of training advice and instruction. Others have assembled their own personalized training courses, and still others have added to their income by writing articles for *Muscle & Fitness*, *Flex*, *Shape*, and other bodybuilding- and sports-conditioning-oriented magazines.

9. *Film work*. This is still an undeveloped source of income, but women bodybuilders like Rachel McLish and Lisa Lyon have made film and television commercial appearances. If you have the type of looks that appeal to a film producer and the type of body that hard training builds, you will have a much better chance of cracking into films than most women. And film work can bring in some big bucks.

We aren't going to claim that every woman who takes up bodybuilding will soon make a living from it. But you *can* make good money from the sport if you have certain genetic

Mary Roberts enjoys her 1981 triumph as the American Lightweight Champ.

Rachel McLish and her mentor, Joe Weider.

advantages physically, you can publicize and market yourself efficiently, and you have the type of drive that it takes to get things done.

THE WEIDER WAY

Over the last 30 years we have trained literally hundreds of thousands of women and millions of men worldwide, teaching them the Weider System of Bodybuilding. A total of nearly 10 million students qualifies us to say that no training system is even close in effectiveness to the Weider System.

Every top woman bodybuilder follows the Weider System in her own workouts, and you should too if you desire to maximize your physical potential.

The remainder of this book is divided into 11 chapters. Chapter 2 deals with more than 10 techniques for increasing training intensity. Chapters 3–9 are devoted to in-depth discussions of how to train each major muscle group, including a variety of result-producing exercises, suggested training routines, and sample routines from the various superstar women bodybuilders. Chapter 10 is concerned with advanced training techniques, Chapter 11 with a detailed discussion of bodybuilding nutrition, and Chapter 12 with a treatment of competitive bodybuilding techniques.

We are certain that you will learn much that will improve your bodybuilding training and diet and that you will soon begin to make even faster progress in your training. Let's get into the gym and do it!

Carla Dunlap rejoices over winning the 1981 American. Shelley Gruwell (right) was runner up.

Susan Roberts, 1983 American Lightweight Champion.

2
SUPERCHARGING YOUR WORKOUT

The techniques explained in this chapter are of paramount importance to any serious bodybuilder because consistent increases in training intensity are necessary if you wish to continue making good gains in muscle mass and quality. Indeed, there is a direct relationship between the amount of training intensity you place on a muscle group and the relative mass and quality of development in that body part.

In this chapter we will first review the topic of resistance progression, then explain the values of training both to the point of momentary muscle failure and past the failure point. We will explain nine Weider Training Principles that can be used to push a working muscle past the point of normal failure, including cheating, forced reps, descending sets, burns, rest-pause sets, negative reps, compound sets, and preexhaustion. And we will conclude this chapter by presenting a formula for total training inten-

sity and a hierarchy of intensity-improving techniques.

High-intensity bodybuilding training *is* painful, and we won't try to kid you by telling you it isn't. The rapid and massive build-up of fatigue toxins within a muscle group during a high-intensity set results in a burning sensation within the muscles. However, the best bodybuilders actually seek out this fatigue pain, which they feel is a sure sign that they are working hard enough to make acceptable gains. And the more often you can push past the pain barrier in an all-out set, the faster you will reach your ultimate bodybuilding goals. One of the most fundamental axioms of bodybuilding, then, is *no pain, no gain*.

PROGRESSION

This will seem like old hat to many readers, but suffice it to say that the object of bodybuilding training is to place progressively greater loads on each working muscle. And there are three ways in which you will progressively increase the resistance you place on a muscle:

1. Do more repetitions with a particular weight than you performed the last time you worked out.
2. Do the same number of repetitions as in a previous workout, but use a heavier weight.
3. Do the same number of sets and reps with the same weight as in a previous training session, but reduce the length of rest intervals between sets.

Decreasing the amount of rest between sets is called *quality training*, and the Weider Quality Training Principle will be discussed in detail in Chapter 12.

In normal bodybuilding training you will use a system of resistance progression in which you incrementally increase both the reps and training poundages used in an exercise. Assuming that you are supposed to do 8 to 12 reps (8 and 12 are respectively called the *lower guide number* and *upper guide number*) in a particular movement, you start your first workout performing eight reps, then add one or two reps to this total during each training session until you can comfortably do 12 repetitions. Then you add five to ten pounds to the bar, drop back to the lower guide number of reps, and begin to work up again to the upper guide number.

With back and lower body exercises, you can safely add 10–20 pounds to the bar or machine you are using each time you increase resistance. And for upper body exercises you probably won't be able to increase the weight by more than 5–10 pounds. However, keep in mind that individual strength levels and potentials vary widely, and you may be able to add more or less weight than was just recommended each time you increase your training resistance.

In Figure 2–1 you will find an example of simple resistance progression over a six-week period of time for one set of 8–12 reps of an Incline Press movement. For the sake of reference, "55 × 8" means you should do

eight reps with 55 pounds.

Past the beginner's stage of training, however, you will do more than one set per exercise, most frequently three or four sets of each movement. In this case you should hit the upper guide number for reps on each set of the movement prior to increasing training resistance. You will find an example of six weeks of progression for four sets of 6–10 reps in the Seated Pulley Row exercise in Figure 2–2.

ADVANCED PROGRESSION

After about one year of training very few women bodybuilders will do all of their sets of a movement with the same weight. Most frequently, an advanced bodybuilder will use a *pyramid* system in which she adds weight to the barbell, dumbbell, or machines she is using in each succeeding set. And while you can do the same number of repetitions for each set while increasing the weight, it's more normal to decrease the weight progressively while increasing the reps. You will find examples of each of these types of pyramids in Figure 2–3.

The advantage of a pyramid system is that it allows you to warm up thoroughly your working muscles and supporting joints with lighter weights before safely attacking maximum poundages. As a result, pyramid training is most frequently used during an off-season cycle when a bodybuilder is working out with very heavy poundages in an effort to further increase her general muscle mass.

There is also a *descending pyramid* system that is used primarily with exercises in which you perform at least 8–10 reps per set. With this system, you will do the same number of reps each set but gradually decrease the amount of weight you are using in the exercise. An example of this descending pyramid system can be found in Figure 2–4.

The descending pyramid is valuable because it accommodates the gradual increase of fatigue and decrease of strength that occurs with each succeeding set that you do for any muscle group. If you wish to use the pyramid and descending pyramid systems in

	Mon	Wed	Fri
Week 1	55 × 8	55 × 9	55 × 10
Week 2	55 × 11	55 × 12	60 × 8
Week 3	60 × 9	60 × 10	60 × 11
Week 4	60 × 12	65 × 8	65 × 9
Week 5	65 × 10	65 × 11	65 × 12
Week 6	70 × 8	70 × 9	70 × 10

Figure 2-1: Progression Example for One Set of 8-12 Reps in the Incline Press.

	Mon	Wed	Fri
Week 1	80 × 8	80 × 10	80 × 11
	80 × 8	80 × 9	80 × 10
	80 × 8	80 × 9	80 × 9
	80 × 8	80 × 8	80 × 9
Week 2	80 × 12	80 × 12	80 × 12
	80 × 11	80 × 12	80 × 12
	80 × 10	80 × 10	80 × 12
	80 × 9	80 × 10	80 × 11
Week 3	80 × 12	90 × 10	90 × 11
	80 × 12	90 × 9	90 × 10
	80 × 12	90 × 8	90 × 9
	80 × 12	90 × 8	90 × 8
Week 4	90 × 11	90 × 12	90 × 12
	90 × 11	90 × 11	90 × 12
	90 × 10	90 × 11	90 × 11
	90 × 8	90 × 9	90 × 10
Week 5	90 × 12	90 × 12	90 × 12
	90 × 12	90 × 12	90 × 12
	90 × 11	90 × 12	90 × 12
	90 × 11	90 × 11	90 × 12
Week 6	100 × 9	100 × 10	100 × 11
	100 × 8	100 × 9	100 × 10
	100 × 8	100 × 9	100 × 9
	100 × 8	100 × 8	100 × 9

Figure 2-2: Progression Example for Four Sets of 6-10 Reps in the Seated Pulley Row.

Consistent Reps

Set Number	Weight	Reps
1	50	10
2	60	10
3	70	10
4	80	10

Decreasing Reps

Set Number	Weight	Reps
1	100	12
2	120	10
3	135	8
4	150	6
5	160	3-4

Figure 2-3: Examples of Weight/Rep Pyramids.

Set Number	Weight	Reps
1	70	10
2	65	10
3	60	10
4	55	10

Figure 2-4: Example of Descending Pyramid.

your own workouts, you can easily use both types of weight-rep schemes for the same body part. For example, you can use a pyramid scheme for Incline Presses in your chest workout, followed by a reverse pyramid system on both Pec Deck Flyes and Cable Crossovers for the same muscle group.

TRAINING TO FAILURE

In order to best use the information presented in the balance of this chapter, you must understand that your muscles will become tougher and more resistant to training as you continue bodybuilding. As a result, you must use greater and greater training intensity to continue forcing them to increase in hypertrophy.

At first, you simply need to go through the motions during a weight workout in order to stimulate your muscles to increase in mass, tone, quality, and strength. But after four to six weeks of low-intensity training, you must begin to push at least one or two exercises for each muscle group to the point of actual momentary muscle failure. And for several months this will guarantee that you continue to make gains from bodybuilding training, particularly if you eventually reach the point where you are taking each post-warm-up set to the failure point.

Undoubtedly there are varying definitions of the failure point, but for our purposes let's consider training to failure as continuing a set in strict form until you fail to complete a repetition. Certainly you will be able to cheat up several more reps, but you won't be able to finish the final repetition in strict biomechanical form.

Kike Elomaa (Miss Olympia) comments on training to failure: "Let's use the Barbell Curl movement as an example of how you should train to failure. Assuming that you can do eight good reps with 55 pounds, grasp the bar, stand erect, and begin doing your reps in a slow, steady manner and with scrupulously strict form.

"The first few reps are relatively easy to perform, but from about the fifth rep on your biceps are burning and the bar moves more and more slowly through the sticking point approximately halfway through the movement when your forearms are parallel to the floor. Finally, on the ninth rep the bar stalls out three or four inches short of the sticking point, and regardless of how hard you exert yourself, you are unable to finish the repetition. This is what is meant by training to the point of momentary muscular failure."

TRAINING PAST FAILURE

After several months of consistently pushing to failure in most of your sets, you should begin to take at least one or two sets for each muscle group *past* the point of failure. Sev-

eral methods of training past failure are presented in the remainder of this chapter. And you definitely should use one or more of these high-intensity Weider Training Principles in your workouts once you have been training to failure for three or four months.

If you use cheating, forced reps, descending sets, or any of several other high-intensity Weider Principles, it *is* possible to force your muscles to keep working with maximum exertion well past the point at which many bodybuilders reach failure and terminate their set. And if you can receive "X" amount of extra benefit from pushing a set to failure, you can receive "2X" or "3X" benefit from continuing a set well past the normal failure point.

Training past failure is the mark of a dedicated woman bodybuilder who either is already a successful competitor or will soon gain great success in competitive bodybuilding. **Rachel McLish** (twice Miss Olympia and a Pro World Champion) is a great example of a woman who consistently trains past failure, and her inspiring physical development is vivid testament to the effectiveness of high-intensity, Weider-style workouts.

In a typical all-out set Rachel will begin by doing several reps to failure in strict form. Then, either she will do many partial reps (called *burns*) to force her muscles to continue exerting or she will have her training partner give her as many forced reps as she can stand while she crashes through the pain barrier. Sometimes Rachel even does negative reps after she's performed as many forced reps as possible, a technique guaranteed to erect an almost impenetrable pain barrier. But by toughing it out, Rachel also smashes through this barrier and takes giant steps toward the physique she believes she will one day have.

Some of the foregoing teminology (e.g., *burns, forced reps, negative reps*) will be unclear to many readers until they have read the discussions of these Weider Training Principles that follow. Still, we hope we have made one crucial point: it's essential for advanced bodybuilders to consistently push at least some sets for each muscle group as far past the failure point as possible. And it will be even better if you can push at least half of your post-warm-up sets past failure. It's only by first pushing to failure and later training past the point of failure that you can develop the ultimate feminine physique.

CHEATING

The Weider Cheating Training Principle is the first method that you will probably use to train past the point of normal momentary muscular failure. It is also the easiest method used to push past failure because you don't need a training partner to help you, as is the case with forced reps, descending sets, and most types of negative reps.

Virtually all beginning and intermediate bodybuilders have been cautioned against cheating in an exercise because lower-level bodybuilders usually unconsciously use extraneous body movement to make an exercise *easier* to do. Therefore, these women should always use very strict form in order to avoid robbing their working muscles of some of the stress they should receive.

Advanced bodybuilders can profitably cheat in an exercise, however, because they do so to make a set much *harder* on their working muscles than is possible in normal training. To use the Weider Cheating Principle correctly you should use the absolute minimum amount of extraneous body motion needed to impart sufficient momentum to the bar to boost it past the sticking point. Each cheating rep should then be finished under your own power and the weight lowered slowly back to the starting point rather than merely dropped back to the starting position.

When discussing how to train to failure, we used the Barbell Curl as an example. In a cheating set of Barbell Curls you would take the same steps discussed earlier to take the set to the point of failure. Then, once you have missed a rep and the bar has returned to the starting point of the exercise, you should use a small amount of torso swing—moving your torso quickly forward and then backward—to boost the bar past the sticking

point of the movement. Use all of your biceps strength to finish the movement, lower the bar slowly back to the starting point, and perform another cheating rep.

Generally speaking, you will probably get near-maximum benefit from doing two or three cheating reps at the end of a set, since your muscles grow fatigued so rapidly past the third or fourth repetition that additional reps are unnecessary. But as with all training techniques, this number varies from individual to individual and you can firmly establish your threshold for reps past the point of failure only through several weeks of experimentation and use of the Weider Instinctive Training Principle.

FORCED REPS

There is one minor disadvantage to using cheating reps to push a set past failure. When you are using extraneous body movement to boost the bar past a sticking point it's impossible to impart exactly the minimum amount necessary just to get the bar past the sticking point. With a few cheating sets of Barbell Curls you'll notice that on some reps you swing the bar so hard that the rep is ridiculously easy to finish, while on others you give it too little momentum and are unable even to get the weight past the sticking point.

The Weider Forced Reps Training Principle gives you a very precise means of essentially removing just enough weight from a bar to allow your fatigued muscles to complete the movement.

Says **Inger Zetterqvist** (Swedish, European, and World Champion): "When you've done six good reps in the Bench Press with 120 pounds and fail on the seventh repetition, what does this mean? It merely means that you can no longer press out 120 pounds, but you could certainly muster up enough strength to do another rep if the bar weighed only 110 and probably a second if the bar weighed 100 pounds. And using some means of removing weight from the bar near the end of a set is the secret behind cheating, forced reps, and other high-intensity training techniques used to continue a set past the point of failure."

With forced reps, unlike with cheating reps, a training partner can pull up on the middle of the bar you're using for Bench Presses with exactly the minimum amount of force necessary to remove just enough weight to allow you to complete a forced rep. And your partner can do this quite easily by applying just enough of an assist to keep the bar moving slowly from the bottom of the exercise to the finish point. This is an especially valuable factor because the geometry of your joints and muscles makes any exercise harder to do at certain points of the complete movement cycle than at others. When cheating, you won't be able to apply a variable removal of weight from the bar, but with forced reps your partner can easily vary the amount of weight he or she removes from the bar.

As with cheating reps, you will probably get the most benefit from doing two or three forced reps past the failure point. But, unlike with the Weider Cheating Principle, you can do forced reps in virtually all exercises, whether they are performed with a barbell, a dumbbell or two, a cable or two, or on an exercise machine. After all, how could you cheat at the end of a set of Squats? You can't, but you could easily have your training partner stand behind you and pull up on either the bar itself or the sides of your waist to help you get a couple of forced reps at the end of a set of Squats.

DESCENDING SETS

You can also use the Weider Descending Sets Training Principle to reduce progressively the amount of weight you are using in an exercise. To illustrate this technique, let's again use the Barbell Curl movement. Load up the bar with a weight that you can use in strict form for about six reps, but be sure to load the bar with plenty of loose plates and leave the collars off the end of the bar.

Take the correct grip on your barbell, stand erect, and do five or six strict reps to the point of failure. Then, without putting the bar down, have two training partners standing at the ends of the bar each remove five or ten pounds of weight. Continue to keep curling the bar with this lighter weight for two or three more reps, again to failure. Have your partners pull off a few more plates and do as many reps as possible with this further reduced poundage.

Normally, you will need only two weight drops, but for exercises that stress the larger muscle groups of your body you might need three or even four weight reductions. Your working muscles will feel like someone is playing a blowtorch across them, but force yourself through this pain barrier and you'll have a great shot at markedly improving your muscular development by using descending sets.

With dumbbell exercises you can provide your own descending sets by merely "going down the rack." To illustrate this technique, let's say you're doing Standing Dumbbell Presses. Start with the heaviest weight you can use and still do four or five strict reps, then take that set to failure. Immediately place the dumbbells back in the rack, pick up the next lightest pair, and do as many reps as you can with these dumbbells. Conclude your descending set with one or two additional weight drops, and your deltoids should be screaming for mercy.

Deborah Diana (U.S. Champion) sums up the value of descending sets: "I do very few sets for each muscle group, seldom more than four to six total sets per body part, so you *know* that each set is taken to the limit. Forced reps are fine, but for real, high-quality muscle tissue I feel that you need to do plenty of descending sets to push your fatigued muscles well past failure. I personally haven't tried an exercise technique that subjects my body to greater training intensity than descending sets!"

BURNS

Burns are quick partial reps normally performed at the starting point or in the finish position of an exercise, and you can most effectively use the Weider Burns Training

Deborah
Diana.

Principle at the conclusion of a set that has already been taken to the point of failure. Tacking eight to ten quick burn reps onto the end of a set to failure results in an incredible stimulation and a huge buildup of fatigue toxins that makes your muscles *burn*, hence the name of the technique.

Let's let **Laura Combes** (the first American Women's Bodybuilding Champion) tell you how to perform burns in your workouts: "I think that it's easiest to learn correct performance of burns in the Standing Calf Raise movement done on a calf machine. Start out by taking a set to failure at between 10 and 15 reps. Then allow your heels to descend as far

as you can get them below the level of your toes. From this position you can bounce your heels upward about two inches with a quick cadence, allowing for a rebound at the bottom of each repetition. The burns have to be quick and bouncy in this position, or you won't get as much out of them. Some bodybuilders do very slow partial movements, but I personally don't feel them as much in my working muscles.

"The number of burns that you do should fall between half the number of full reps you performed and the actual number of full reps. So, you might do 10 full reps of Calf Raises followed up by five to ten burns. And

Laura Combes.

believe me, it *does* burn like the fires of Hades. Stick it out, however, and you'll get an incredible amount of development from this technique."

Rachel McLish does a different type of burn in her workouts, one that commences before she has reached the point of failure in a set. After four or five good reps she will locate what she feels is the most productive range of her exercise and do several slow burns in this position, each movement three or four inches long. Often this productive part of the exercise will be at the fully contracted position of the movement, but

equally as often it will be at some other point along the exercise's full range of motion.

REST-PAUSE WORKOUTS

The Weider Rest-Pause Training Principle was presented on the pages of *Your Physique* magazine, the forerunner of *Muscle & Fitness*, during the early 1950s, but the technique failed to gain popularity until 30 years later. This is a mystery to us, since rest-pause workouts are the ultimate technique for building maximum muscle mass and strength.

No bodybuilder can deny that you must lift maximum weights for four to six reps in strict form in order to develop optimum mass and power. But fatigue sets in so quickly with absolute maximum poundages that it's difficult to perform more than two or three reps with these huge weights.

It takes very little rest time between sets for a muscle to regain its preeffort amount of strength and endurance. In fact, with just 10–15 seconds of rest between sets, you will recoup a minimum of 50 percent of your strength and endurance. Therefore, it makes good sense to use maximum weights for several different approaches to the bar, taking only a 10- to 15-second rest-pause between "sets." In this way, you can essentially perform five to eight "reps" in stages for a single set with totally awesome weights, the basic premise of rest-pause training.

Let's use the Incline Press with a barbell as an example of rest-pause training in action. Warm up thoroughly by performing two or three high-rep sets with progressively heavier weights in each set to ensure freedom from joint and muscle injuries once you tackle the heaviest weights. Then load up the bar with a poundage that allows you just to squeeze out two or three superhard reps.

Lie back on the bench, take your grip, lift the bar off the rack, and force out your two or three reps. Place the bar back on the rack, but don't take your hands off the bar during your rest-pause of 10–15 seconds. Pick up the bar again and force out as many reps as possible, which will probably be only one or two. At this point, you will probably be forced to reduce the weight on the bar by about 10 percent, but be sure you still take only a 10- to 15-second rest-pause, even if you must have a training partner standing by to assist you in quickly changing the weight on your bar.

With the new weight you can probably again force out two or three reps, after which you should again take a short rest-pause, followed by a final brutally difficult one or two reps. So, in total, you will perform a "set" of 6–10 tough reps with absolutely maximum poundages.

Rest-pause training will give you incredibly quick results because it is of ultimate high intensity, but no one can train with rest-pause sets during every workout without soon overtraining. We suggest that you try one set of rest-pause work on a single basic exercise per body part only once every two weeks for each muscle group. And you should not attempt to use rest-pause sets until you have a minimum of one year of steady, high-intensity workouts under your belt.

NEGATIVE REPS

The Weider Retro-Gravity Training Principle encompases all ramifications of negative-rep training in your workouts, and in this section we will discuss four distinct ways in which you can work the negative (downward) half of a repetition even harder than you stress the positive (upward) half of a movement.

Two decades ago exercise physiologists discovered that the negative cycle of an exercise offered at least as much potential for strength and muscular development as the positive cycle of the movement. And thousands of Weider-trained bodybuilders worldwide make intelligent use of negative-rep training to achieve maximum physical development.

The easiest way to emphasize the negative cycle of an exercise is simply to be certain to lower the weight more slowly than you raise it on each repetition. We recommend taking

three to four seconds to raise a weight and six to eight seconds to lower it when attempting to emphasize the negative cycle of an exercise. So, it's always a good practice to lower the weight slowly in every post-warm-up set that you perform in your workouts.

Although it's quite difficult to obtain training partners who will sacrifice their own workouts to help you, it's possible to perform pure negative reps in which your partners raise a heavier-than-normal weight for you to lower slowly on your own, while mightily resisting the downward force of the weight. If you can cadge training partners for pure negatives once each week or two, you'll make very fast gains, but again it's difficult to talk other bodybuilders into assisting you in this manner.

With a single training partner, however, you can use a technique called *forced negatives*. This involves raising the weight in an exercise on your own, then resisting the downward pressure of both the weight itself and the resistance added by your partner's pushing down against the bar or other type of weight you are using.

Candy Csencsits (runner-up, Miss Olympia) explains: "In my own workouts I can conveniently add negative reps to bring out greater mass and muscular detail by having my husband, Frank, push down on the weight I'm using during the negative cycle of each repetition. I'd estimate that using this forced negative reps technique has added at least 10 percent to the mass and quality of my physique, moving me up from sixth to second place in the Miss Olympia competition in a single year."

As long as you are performing machine exercises, you can provide yourself with a type of negative resistance called by many bodybuilders *self-paced negative-empha-sized reps*, or merely *negative emphasis repetitions*. With this technique you raise the weight with both arms or legs and then lower it with only one limb, resisting the doubled weight as powerfully as possible. Naturally, you won't be able to use negative emphasis reps with free weights because you'd look kind of silly trying to lower a barbell in a

Candy Csencsits.

Barbell Curl movement with only one hand placed far off center on the bar. But with machines you can easily use the negative emphasis technique.

Shelley Gruwell (World Grand Prix Champion) comments on her use of negative emphasis reps: "During phases when I can't work out with a training partner I'll make good use of negative emphasized reps. A good example of this technique is when I do Calf Presses on a leg press machine. With both feet I'll push the weight as far away from myself as I can; then I'll remove pressure from my left foot and lower the weight while resisting it with just the strength of my right calf. On the next rep I'll again push it out with both feet, but this time I lower it with just my left foot. By alternating feet, I can stress my calf muscles with incredible intensity. And that spells results!"

COMPOUND SETS

The three types of compound sets (supersets, trisets, and giant sets) discussed in this section do not allow you to push a set past failure, but they do add appreciably to the overall intensity of your workouts. This is due to what is essentially a shorter average rest interval between sets. You may discover that compound sets work best for your unique body prior to a competition, but many bodybuilders use compound sets extensively in the off-season.

The most fundamental type of compound sets is a superset, or a grouping of two exercises with a minimum amount of rest between movements, all followed by a rest interval of normal length. The least intense form of superset consists of one movement each for such antagonistic muscle groups as

---

Figure 2-5: Examples of Supersets for Antagonistic Muscle Groups.

Chest + Back = Bench Presses + Lat Pulldowns
Quads + Hamstrings = Leg Extensions + Leg Curls
Biceps + Triceps = Barbell Curls + Pulley Pushdowns
Chest + Back = Parallel Bar Dips + Chins behind Neck
Quads + Hamstrings = Leg Presses + Stiff-Leg Deadlifts
Biceps + Triceps = Dumbbell Curls + Lying Triceps Extensions
Forearm Flexors + Forearm Extensors = Wrist Curls + Reverse Wrist Curls

the biceps and triceps, pectorals and lats, quadriceps and hamstrings, or the forearm flexors and forearm extensors. You will find examples of this type of superset in Figure 2-5 above.

A more intense form of superset involves performing two consecutive exercises for the same muscle group. You will find this type of superset to be particularly effective when used for large muscle groups such as the thighs, back and chest. A special type of superset involving two movements for the same body part is called *preexhaustion supersetting*, which is discussed in detail in the following section of this chapter. You will find several examples of supersets for a single muscle group in Figure 2-6.

Stepping up in intensity from supersets, you come to trisets, or groupings of three exercises with no rest between movements, followed by a normal rest interval and a second triset. Trisets are particularly effective for use on large, multifaceted muscle groups like the pecs, delts, lats, and quads. You will find examples of trisets in Figure 2-7.

Stepping up in intensity one more time, you can perform giant sets, or groupings of four to six exercises with little or no rest between movements, all followed by a rest interval of normal duration. You can do giant sets for either a single muscle group or two antagonistic body parts. And the more exercises in a giant set, the greater the intensity of that compound set. You will find examples of various giant sets in Figure 2-8.

Figure 2-6: Examples of Supersets for a Single Muscle Group.

Pectorals = Incline Presses + Pec Deck Flyes
Traps = Upright Rows + Dumbbell Shrugs
Lats = Lat Pulldowns + Cross-Bench Pullovers
Biceps = Barbell Preacher Curls + Standing Barbell Curls
Triceps = Parallel Bar Dips + Pulley Pushdowns
Quads = Squats + Leg Extensions
Hamstrings = Stiff-Leg Deadlifts + Leg Curls
Calves = Standing Calf Raises + Seated Calf Raises

Figure 2-7: Examples of Trisets.

Deltoids
Military Presses (anterior deltoid heads)
Side Laterals (medial deltoid heads)
Dumbbell Bent Laterals (posterior deltoid heads)

Pectorals
Incline Presses (upper pectorals)
Decline Flyes (lower and outer pectorals)
Cross-Bench Pullovers (full pectoral mass and ribcage)

Back
Front Chins (lats)
Barbell Shrugs (traps)
Hyperextensions (erectors)

Thighs
Leg Presses (quadriceps mass)
Leg Curls (hamstring development)
Leg Extensions (quadriceps shape and cuts)

Figure 2-8: Examples of Giant Sets.

Four Exercises for Antagonistic Muscle Groups
Incline Presses (upper pecs)
Lat Pulldowns (lat width)
Parallel Bar Dips (lower and outer pecs)
Seated Pulley Rows (lat thickness)

Four Exercises for a Single Muscle Group
Chins behind Neck (lat width)
Dumbbell Shrugs (taps)
Hyperextensions (erectors)
Seated Pulley Rows (lat thickness)

Five Exercises for a Single Muscle Group
Bench Press (general pectoral mass)
Decline Flyes (lower and outer pecs)
Cross-Bench Pullovers (general pec development, serratus, ribcage expansion)
Pec Deck Flyes (inner pecs)
Cable Crossovers (pectoral detail)

Six Exercises for Antagonistic Muscle Groups
Bench Presses (pec mass)
Front Chins (lat width)
Parallel Bar Dips (lower and outer pecs)
Seated Pulley Rowing (lat width)
Pec Deck Flyes (inner pecs)
Stiff-Arm Pulldowns (lower lats and serratus)

Six Exercises for a Single Muscle Group
Chins behind Neck (lat width)
Stiff-Leg Deadlifts (erectors)
Barbell Bent Rowing (lat thickness)
Dumbbell Shrugs (traps)
Nautilus Pullovers (general lat development and serratus)
Upright Rows (traps and upper back)

PREEXHAUSTION

The Weider Preexhaustion Training Principle is very effectively used to stress torso muscle groups (pecs, lats, traps, and delts) with much more intensity than is normally possible. And you should incorporate preex-

haustion supersets into your workouts as soon as you can accept their markedly greater intensity.

The problem with many basic exercises for your torso muscle groups is that your arms are also involved in the movement along with your pecs, lats, traps, or delts. And since your biceps and triceps are much smaller and weaker than the torso groups, your arms fatigue and give out long before you work your pecs, lats, traps, and delts as hard as you should to induce maximum development in these torso body parts.

By supersetting an isolation movement that doesn't involve the arm muscles for a torso group with a basic exercise that uses the arms for the same body part, you can effectively preexhaust the torso group with the isolation movement. This makes your torso group briefly weaker than your arms, which in turn allows you to use your arms in the basic movement to push your pecs, lats, traps, or delts far deeper into the pain zone than previously possible.

You will discover several examples of preexhaustion supersets in Figure 2-9. You can gradually begin to integrate these preexhaustion supersets into your overall training philosophy.

TOTAL TRAINING INTENSITY

There are myriad ways in which you can

Figure 2-9: Examples of Preexhaustion Supersets.

Upper Pectorals = Incline Flyes + Incline Barbell Presses
Lower Pectorals = Decline Flyes + Decline Barbell Presses
Pectorals (in general) = Flat-Bench Flyes + Bench Presses
Deltoids = Side Laterals + Presses behind Neck
Deltoids = Upright Rows + Military Presses
Lats = Cross-Bench Pullovers + Seated Pulley Rows
Lats = Nautilus Pullovers + Lat Pulldowns
Traps = Barbell Shrugs + Barbell Upright Rows

combine the high-intensity training techniques discussed in this chapter to place total intensity on a working muscle group. However, we can give you one easy method through which you can achieve maximum intensity using only a single training partner. For this purpose, let's use the Barbell Preacher Curl.

Load a weight on the bar that limits you to five or six strict full-range repetitions, grasp the bar, assume the correct position on a preacher bench, and curl the weight up and down until you reach failure. As soon as you reach the failure point, your partner should give you two or three forced reps, but with a forced negative added to the downward cycle of the movement. Finally, when your biceps are almost completely exhausted, your partner can lift the weight up to the finish position of the movement to allow you three or four pure negative reps.

At the end of this set you will have saturation-bombed your biceps to the point where they literally are unable to continue contracting. This process will be highly painful, but it yields such great results that you can achieve an optimum biceps workout with only three to five of these total intensity sets during each training session. Give this formula a try!

A HIERARCHY OF INTENSITY TECHNIQUES

It's essential that you avoid harmfully shocking your muscles by trying out an advanced intensity technique before you have laid the proper groundwork of steady training on techniques of lesser intensity. Therefore, you must keep in mind that you should first train for two or three months merely pushing most of your sets to the point of failure before you begin to extend a few sets past the normal failure point.

The first past-failure technique that you should use is cheating reps, followed two or three months later by forced reps and still later by descending sets and perhaps also a few burns. Supersets should be kicked in at about this point, followed two or three months later by preexhaustion supersets. And a bit later you can also give trisets and giant sets a trial. Next you can do negative reps, but avoid doing rest-pause workouts until you have at least one year of steady, maximum-intensity workouts behind you.

Dr. Lynne Pirie.

3

WORLD-CLASS LEGS

With suitable effort and attention to detail, virtually any woman bodybuilder can develop excellent hip and thigh musculature, even if genetics seem to make these body parts weak. A good example of a woman who has overcome less desirable thigh and hip development is Carla Dunlap, winner of the Miss Olympia, Pro World Championship, and Caesar's Palace Pro Invitational titles. Carla had very weak leg and buttocks development, but through hard training was able to build up these areas to rival the mass and muscularity of the balance of her physique.

Many other women have taken good to excellent physical potential in their thighs and hips and built world-class legs. A few of these are Rachel McLish (Miss Olympia, Pro World Champion), Lori Bowen (American and Pro World Champion), Inger Zetterqvist (World Champion), and Lynn Conkwright (Pro World Champion, Pro World Couples Champion). From this list, it should be obvious that most women can develop incredible hip and thigh muscles.

As a competitive bodybuilder, your goal should be to train your thighs and hips with maximum intensity and work loads, bringing them up to a degree of mass and quality that will bring gasps of amazement from the audience when you do your free-posing program. But you should not build up your thighs and hips to the level that they overshadow either your calves or your upper body.

The primary reason that bodybuilders fail to achieve optimum hip and leg development is that they fail to train these large muscle groups as hard as they need to be hit to stimulate maximum growth. It's painful to do a tough leg workout, so many lazy bodybuilders fail to put out sufficient energy to stimulate optimum growth. You'll never develop an earthshaking physique without doing plenty of heavy Squats in your leg and hip routines.

The muscles of your thighs and hip girdle are important in virtually all sports, either directly or in a supporting role while other muscles carry the load. Our theory of sports conditioning is that a chain is only as strong as its weakest link, so an athlete should take care to strengthen every part of her body.

Health- and fitness-minded women should strengthen their legs and hips in order to maintain cardiorespiratory fitness and health, as well as to help avoid developing cellulite on your thighs and buttocks. Both high-resistance bodybuilding movements and low-intensity aerobic training should be included in your leg workouts.

THIGH AND HIP ANATOMY AND KINESIOLOGY

There are four main muscle groups in your thighs—the quadriceps on the front of your thigh, the biceps femoris on the back of your thigh, the leg adductors on the inner side of your thigh, and the leg abductors on the outer side of your thigh and hip. Of course, there are several other smaller groups, but they will be completely developed if you merely pay close attention to including exercises for each of the four main leg muscle groups in your training programs.

The quadriceps muscle has four lobes, and it contracts primarily to straighten your leg from a bent position. You'll often hear this group referred to as your *quads*. Secondary functions of your quads are thigh adduction and rotation of your thigh within your hip socket.

Your biceps femoris (also called your *leg biceps*, *thigh biceps*, or *hamstrings*) consists of two lobes and contracts to bend your leg from a straight position.

The adductor and abductor muscles of your thighs help to pull your leg either toward the center line of your body (adduction) or away from the center line of your body (abduction). The adductor muscles cover both your upper/outer thighs and hips. The hip abductors serve the same func-

tion as the thigh abductors.

The final muscle group that should concern you is the gluteus maximus ("glutes") that form your buttocks. This large, rounded muscle group contracts primarily to help move your thigh bone into a straight line with your torso from a position in which your thigh is at less than a 90-degree angle with your torso.

THIGH AND HIP TRAINING SECRETS

You'll undoubtedly gain your best results in thigh and hip training if you attack these complex muscle groups from a wide variety of angles. From the discussion of thigh anatomy, for example, you should understand that you require at least one exercise to stress each of the four major areas of your thigh musculature—quads, hamstrings, adductors, and abductors. And in all likelihood, you'll need two or more movements for your hamstrings and three or four more for your quads when you're preparing for a competition.

Many bodybuilders make the mistake of concentrating most of their energy on either heavy Squats or heavy Leg Presses in their thigh and hip workouts. Such a training philosophy will certainly yield massive thigh development, but it will be development that is devoid of significant muscular detail. So, when you're making up your leg workouts you'll need to include exercises for both muscle mass and muscular detail.

Never neglect working to perfect the development of your hip and buttock muscles, or your physique will look weak from several angles onstage. Rachel McLish is one woman bodybuilder who has consistently performed high-intensity hip and buttock workouts, which have in turn given her one of the most shapely tushes in the sport. Oh, yes, Rachel has won *two* Miss Olympia titles, too!

THIGH AND HIP EXERCISES

It's essential that you correctly master each thigh and hip exercise described and illustrated in this section. If you don't do the

Squats—start, left; finish, below.

movements correctly, you will receive less than optimum developmental value from them. And since it's very difficult to unlearn bad exercise habits, it's best to learn the exercises correctly from the very start of your involvement in bodybuilding.

Squats

Emphasis—This is the single best lower body exercise, and many competitive body-builders consider Squats to be the best of all bodybuilding movements. Squats place very intense stress on your quads, buttocks, lower back, and thigh adductors. Secondary stress is on your hamstrings, upper back muscles, and abdominals.

Starting Position—Load a barbell resting on a squat rack with a poundage that will tax your leg muscles. Place your feet about shoulder-width apart directly beneath the bar, grasp the ends of the bar out near the plates, and duck your head under the bar to position it across your trapezius muscles behind your neck. Flatten your back and straighten your legs to remove the weight from the rack, then step back one or two paces from the rack. Set your feet about shoulder width apart again, your toes either pointed straight ahead or angled slightly

Julie McNew demonstrates Half Squats.

Repeat the movement for the suggested number of reps.

Exercise Variations—Although we don't feel that you'll get much out of Partial Squats, many bodybuilders like to do Quarter Squats, Half Squats, Parallel Squats, or Bench Squats once per week in an effort to foster even greater thigh mass. In Quarter and Half Squats you sink only a quarter or half of the way into a full squatting position. With Parallel Squats you sink down only until your thighs are parallel with the floor. And with Bench Squats you straddle a flat exercise bench and descend only until your buttocks lightly touch the bench (the bench can be set at a variety of depths).

Training Tips—To protect your lower back and abdomen from injury when squatting with maximum poundages, you should wear a leather weightlifting belt cinched tightly around your waist. And to protect your knees, you can wrap elastic gauze bandages around the joints. Finally, all variations of the Squat should be performed flat-footed, although with inflexible ankles you might need to do your Squats with your heels elevated on a two-by-four-inch board or two thick barbell plates.

Front Squats

Emphasis—The effect of Front Squats is similar to that of normal back Squats, except that more stress is placed on the lower section of the quadriceps group just above the knee with Front Squats and less strain is placed on the lower back.

Starting Position—Place a moderately weighted barbell on a squat rack. Step up to the bar and extend your arms straight forward from your shoulders and parallel with the floor. Move your arms beneath the bar and position it across your upper chest and shoulders, bending your knees to an appropriate degree. Cross your forearms over the bar and keep your elbows up throughout the movement. As long as you don't allow your elbows to drop, the bar will remain securely in position. Place your feet directly beneath the bar, straighten your legs to lift the bar off

outward. Keep your back flat, your head up, and your torso upright throughout your set. If the bar cuts painfully into your neck in this position, you can pad the bar by rolling a towel around it. And if you seem to experience difficulty in keeping your torso upright as you do your set of Squats, try focusing your eyes on a point at head level throughout each repetition.

The Movement—Slowly bend your legs and sink into a deep squatting position with the bar across your upper back. Your knees should travel directly out over your toes as you do the movement. Without bouncing in the bottom position, slowly recover to the starting point by straightening your legs.

Front Squats—start, left; finish, below.

the rack, and step back one or two paces from the squat rack. Place your feet about shoulder width apart, your toes angled slightly outward. Keep your head up and your torso erect throughout the movement.

The Movement—Being sure that your knees travel outward directly over your toes, slowly bend your legs and sink into a full squatting position. Without bouncing at the bottom of the movement, straighten your legs and return to the starting position. Repeat the movement for the suggested number of repetitions.

Training Tips—It is more likely that you will need to wear a weightlifting belt and stand with your heels elevated when doing Front Squats than when doing Squats. And you will find that you can use only about two-thirds the amount of weight for Front Squats as for Squats.

Leg Presses

Emphasis—There are several types of machines on which you can perform Leg Presses. Regardless of the machine used for

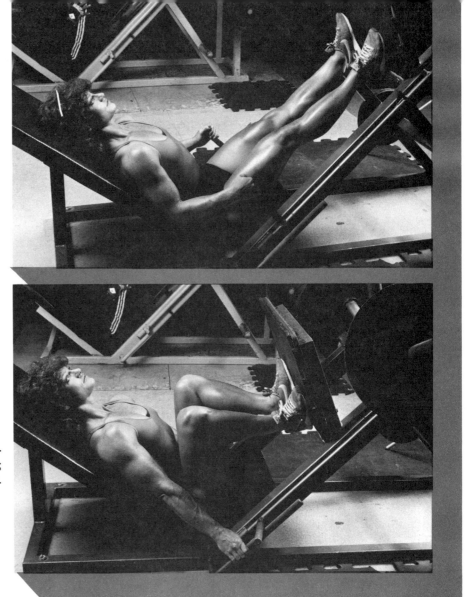

Leg Press (on 45-degree-angled machine)—start, top; finish, bottom.

this movement, you can use Leg Presses to stress your quadriceps intensely and place secondary emphasis on your hamstrings. Unlike when Squatting, Leg Presses allow you to place very intense stress on your quads without also involving your lower back in the movement.

Starting Position—Let's use the popular 45-degree-angled leg press machine to illustrate how to perform this movement. Sit in the machine seat with your back on the angled surface (which is usually padded), your butt in the corner formed by the back rest and the seat rest, and your upper legs angled up the other angled surface of the machine. Place your feet on the sliding platform about shoulder width apart, your toes either pointed directly ahead or angled slightly outward. Straighten your legs and then rotate the stop bars at the sides of the machine to free the weight. Grasp either the stop bars or the handles provided near your hips to secure your upper body in the machine during your set.

The Movement—Without moving anything but your legs, slowly bend your legs and allow the weighted platform to descend slowly down the angled runners until it reaches the lowest possible position. Slowly straighten your legs to return to the starting point and repeat the movement for the suggested number of reps.

Training Tips—A very similar (and somewhat older vintage) leg press machine allows you to do this exercise while lying on your back and pushing the platform upward along vertically set runners. And with both the Nautilus and Universal Gym leg press machines you can do the movement while seated erect.

Hack Squats—start, left; finish, right.

Hack Squats

Emphasis—Hacks intensely stress the quadriceps, particularly the quads just above your kness and the long outer sweep of the muscle group. Secondary stress is placed on your hamstrings and buttocks.

Starting Position—There are two types of hack machine, but we'll use the yoke-type machine for our primary discussion. Back up to the machine and bend your legs so you can place your shoulders comfortably up under the yokes. Position your feet shoulder width apart on the angled foot platform, then straighten your legs. Rotate the stop bars at the sides of the platform to the sides to release the weight for your exercise.

The Movement—Slowly bend your legs and lower the weight downward until your legs are fully bent. Without bouncing in the bottom position of the exercise, slowly return to the starting point and repeat the movement for the suggested number of counts.

Training Tips—You will no doubt encounter another type of hack machine in which you lie back against a sliding platform and grasp handles by the sides of your hips to add resistance to the movement. Regardless of the type of hack machine utilized, you should work with a variety of foot positions, changing stance width and toe angle (inward, straight ahead, outward).

Lunges

Emphasis—Lunges are great for cutting up your quads, particularly the upper section of the muscle group where your quadriceps run into an insertion at your pelvic girdle. Quite strong stress is also placed on the buttocks and upper hamstrings.

Starting Position—Place a light barbell across your shoulders as if for the start of a set of Squats and balance it in position by grasping the bar out near the plates. Set your feet about six inches apart, your toes pointed straight ahead, and stand erect.

The Movement—Step about two and a half or three feet straight forward with your left foot, being sure your toes are pointed straight ahead as you position your foot on the floor. Keeping your right leg held rela-

tively straight, slowly bend your left leg as fully as possible. In the bottom position of the movement, your left knee will be several inches in front of your left ankle, and your right knee will be three or four inches from the floor. Push off with your left foot to return to the starting point and repeat the exercise, alternating front foot (right, left, right, etc.) until you're performed the desired number of reps with each leg held forward.

Training Tips—Rather than holding a light barbell across your shoulders, you can do your Lunges while holding a pair of light dumbbells at straight arms' length down at your sides. You can also vary the length of your forward set, regardless of whether you're using a barbell or two light dumbbells.

Lunges—start, left; finish, right.

Sissy Squats

Emphasis—Sissy Squats are a very intense quadriceps exercise that is used primarily just prior to a competition to improve frontal thigh cuts. There is very little involvement of any other muscle group in this unique exercise.

Starting Position—There are several methods of performing this exercise, but you'll find it easiest to balance during the exercise if you perform it between a set of parallel bars, which you can grasp to help steady your body. Stand with your feet about eight inches apart, your toes pointed directly forward between the bars, and grasp the parallel bars lightly with your hands for the exercise.

The Movement—You must simultaneously perform four functions for this movement to be effective: (1) Slowly bend your legs as fully as possible. (2) Rise up on your toes. (3) Thrust your knees as far forward over your feet as is comfortably possible. (4) Incline your torso backward until it is just above a position parallel with the floor. You'll feel a very intense stretching sensation in your quads at the bottom point of the movement when you're doing it correctly. Slowly return to the starting position and repeat the exercise for an appropriate number of repetitions.

Training Tips—If you don't experience much difficulty in balancing this movement, you can do it while holding on to a sturdy upright with just one hand. This one-handed version of the exercise allows you to add resistance by holding a loose barbell plate against your chest during the set you are performing.

Sissy Squat at midpoint.

Leg Extensions

Emphasis—Leg Extensions allow you to place very direct, intense, and isolated stress on your quadriceps muscles. Leg Extensions are a particularly good movement for carving deep grooves of muscular detail between the individual segments of your quadriceps group.

Starting Position—Sit in the leg machine seat and adjust the seat back forward and backward (use the lever at the right side of the machine) until you can sit with your back against the pad and still fit your knees snugly against the edge of the seat pad. Hook your toes beneath the roller pads, fasten the seat belt over your lap, and grasp the handles beside your hips to steady your body in position as you do the movement.

The Movement—Use quadriceps strength to straighten your legs slowly. Pause in this top position for a slow count of two to enhance the peak contraction effect in your quads, return to the starting point, and repeat the exercise for an appropriate number of reps.

Training Tips—You can intensify the effect of this exercise on your quads by doing it with one leg at a time. In all exercises performed with one arm or leg you achieve a more pronounced contraction in the working muscles because your mental focus need not be split between the two sides of your body. Instead, you get a double-force contraction on just one side of your body at a time. Whether you use one leg or two for the movement, you can vary the effect of Leg Curls on your quads by changing your toe angle as you do the movement. Most bodybuilders do all of their Leg Extensions with their toes pointed directly upward at the top of the movement, but you can also do some sets with your toes angled slightly outward and others with your toes angled slightly inward during the exercise.

Leg Extensions—start, left; finish, below.

Lying Leg Curls—start, above; finish, below.

Lying Leg Curls

Emphasis—Both Lying and Standing Leg Curls stress your hamstrings in almost complete isolation from the remainder of your body.

Starting Position—As with Leg Extensions, you can perform Lying Leg Curls on a variety of machines, but we'll describe the Nautilus movement since it is representative of all other Leg Curl variations. Lie facedown on the padded surface of the bench, your knees at the edge of the pad toward the lever arm of the machine. Hook your heels beneath the roller pads attached to the lever arm of the machine, grasp the handles provided at the sides of the padded surface, and fully straighten your legs. It's important that you press your hips firmly against the pad and hold them down in this position throughout the exercise.

The Movement—Slowly bend your legs as completely as possible, hold the top position of the movement for a slow count of two to enhance its peak contraction effect, return to the starting point, and repeat the exercise for the suggested number of repetitions.

Training Tips—As with Leg Extensions, you can perform Lying Leg Curls with one leg at a time as well as with alternative foot positions.

Standing Leg Curls—start, left; finish, right.

Standing Leg Curls

Emphasis—In recent years an apparatus has evolved that allows you to perform Leg Curls with one leg at a time in a standing position. And since the movement can be performed one-legged, it is of somewhat greater intensity for your biceps femoris group than the normal two-legged version of Lying Leg Curls.

Starting Position—Stand slightly to the right side of the machine and place your left leg in the apparatus so your left knee rests against the restraining pad and the back of your left ankle rests against the roller pad. Fully straighten your leg and grasp the part of the upper section of the machine to restrain your body in the correct exercise position as you do your set.

The Movement—Use hamstring strength to bend your leg slowly as fully as possible. Hold the top position of the movement for a slow count of two to enhance the peak contraction effect of the exercise, lower back to the starting point, and repeat the exercise for the suggested number of repetitions. Be sure to do an equal number of sets and reps with each leg.

Training Tips—As with Lying Leg Curls, you should occasionally vary your foot position to reach unique new areas of your leg biceps.

Stiff-Leg Deadlifts

Emphasis—This variation of the Deadlift places maximum stress on your hamstrings as well as on the spinal erectors and buttocks. Secondary stress is placed on your upper back and forearm muscle groups.

Starting Position—Place a moderately weighted barbell across a flat exercise bench. Stand on the exercise bench with your feet about six inches apart and take a shoulder-width overgrip on the barbell handle. With your legs bent, lift the weight up to your thighs and straighten your entire body. Be sure to keep your arms and legs held straight as you do Stiff-Leg Deadlifts.

The Movement—Keeping your back as flat as possible, slowly bend over at the waist and lower the barbell downward as far as you comfortably can. Ideally, you'll be able to touch the bar to your toes comfortably. Slowly recover to the starting position and repeat the movement. Since your lower back is in a relatively weak mechanical position when your legs are held straight, it's essential that you do this movement slowly and with no abrupt jerks along its range of motion.

Training Tips—For a unique feel in your hamstrings and erectors, you can perform Stiff-Leg Deadlifts while holding two moderately heavy dumbbells in your hands. You could perform barbell Stiff-Leg Deadlifts standing on the floor, but the diameter of the plates on the barbell would terminate the movement short of its potential range of motion. Therefore, you should always do Stiff-Leg Deadlifts while standing on an exercise bench or a thick block of wood.

Stiff-Leg Deadlift—start, top right; finish, bottom right.

Cable Leg Adduction at finish.

leg away from the left as far as is comfortably possible. From this starting point, use inner thigh power to pull your right leg toward the left either until your legs touch each other or until you have pulled your right leg as far as possible across the midline of your body in front of your stationary left leg. Return to the starting point and repeat the exercise for the required number of reps.

Movement (Leg Abduction)—Attach the cuff to your right ankle, but stand with your left side toward the pulley, the weight pulling your right leg somewhat across your left leg. Use hip and thigh abductor strength to move your stationary right leg out to the side and upward as high as you comfortably can. Return to the starting point and repeat the movement.

Cable Leg Abduction at finish.
(Maria Gonzalez is model.)

Cable Leg/Hip Movements

Emphasis—Depending on which direction you move your foot under resistance with these exercises, you can work your adductor, abductor, quadriceps, or buttock muscles.

Movement (Leg Adduction)—Fasten a padded cuff to your right ankle and attach a floor pulley cable to the cuff. Stand with your right side to the machine, bracing your body in position by grasping a sturdy upright. Hold both legs straight during the movement. With your left foot firmly planted on the floor, allow the weight to pull your right

Movement (Forward Leg Kick)—Attach the cuff to your right ankle and stand facing directly away from the floor pulley, the weight pulling your straight right leg backward as far as is comfortably possible. Brace your body in this position. Using quadriceps strength, slowly move your straight right leg forward and upward to as high a position as is comfortably possible. Return to the starting point and repeat the exercise. Alternatively, you can raise your leg forward with your knee bent to about a 30-degree angle, then finish the movement by straightening your leg as if kicking at a soccer ball.

Movement (Rear Leg Kick)—Attach the cuff to your right ankle and stand facing directly toward the floor pulley, the weight

Cable Rear Leg Kick.

Cable Forward Leg Kick.

pulling your straight right leg forward as far as is comfortably possible. Brace your body in this position. Using buttock strength, slowly move your straight right leg backward and upward to as high a position as is comfortably possible. Return to the starting point and repeat the exercise.

Training Tips—Be sure to do an equal number of sets and reps for each side of your body on every movement. You might find it a bit more comfortable to perform each of these exercises if you stand with your support (stationary) foot on a block of wood or barbell plate to keep your free foot from brushing the floor on each repetition.

SUGGESTED THIGH AND HIP ROUTINES

While this book is intended primarily for intermediate and advanced weight trainers and bodybuilders, there may be a few beginners reading this chapter. We define a beginner as any woman with less than six to eight weeks of training experience behind her. Following is a beginning-level leg program that can be used on three nonconsecutive days per week:

Exercise	Sets	Reps
Leg Presses	3	10-15
Leg Curls	2-3	10-15
Lunges	1-2	10-15

After you have completed six to eight weeks of the foregoing program you can move up to the following low-intermediate routine, which you can perform on three nonconsecutive days per week:

Exercise	Sets	Reps
Leg Extensions	2-3	10-15
Squats	3-4	10-15
Stiff-Legged Deadlifts	2-3	10-15
Standing Leg Curls	2-3	10-15
Rear Leg Kicks	1-2	10-15

Another six to eight weeks of training will bring you to the full intermediate level of training. At that point you can use the following thigh and hip routine on three nonconsecutive days per week:

Exercise	Sets	Reps
Leg Extensions	3-4	10-15
Hack Squats	3-4	10-15
Lunges	3-4	10-15
Stiff-Legged Deadlifts	3-4	10-15
Lying Leg Curls	3-4	10-15
Cable Leg Abductions	1-2	10-15
Cable Leg Adductions	1-2	10-15
Cable Front Leg Kicks	1-2	10-15
Cable Rear Leg Kicks	1-2	10-15

LEG AND HIP ROUTINES OF THE CHAMPIONS

It's important to understand that the routines presented in this section are of extremely high intensity. If you have less than a year of solid, all-out training behind you, you won't make good gains using any of these programs. And it's likely that you will soon overtrain using one of these routines, which can even lead to a regression in your physical development. However, by scaling these routines down to your own ability levels, you *can* make good progress with them. Simply do the same exercises as your favorite champion, but perform fewer sets of each movement.

Pillow
(Gold's Classic Champion)

Exercise	Sets	Reps
Angled Leg Presses	5	12-6*
Leg Extensions	4-5	8-10
Hack Squats	4-5	8-10
Lying Leg Curls	5-8	8-10
Standing Leg Curls	5-8	8-10
Cable Leg Adductions	4-5	8-10
Cable Leg Abductions	4-5	8-10

* This exercise is performed with weights and reps pyramided.

Deborah Diana
(Ms. USA)

Exercise	Sets	Reps
Leg Presses	1	10-15
Leg Extensions	1	10-15
Leg Curls	1	10-15
Squats	1	10-15

All sets are taken to failure; this program is performed as a giant set.

Kike Elomaa
(Miss Olympia)

Exercise	Sets	Reps
Squats (warm-up)	1	20
Nautilus Leg Presses	3	12-15
Nautilus Leg Extensions	3	12-15
Nautilus Leg Curls	3	12-15

Sherry Atton.

Madeline Almeida
(Ms. Eastern America)

Exercise	Sets	Reps
Leg Extensions	4	10–12
Leg Presses	4	10–12
Leg Curls	3	10–12
Lunges	2	10–15

Debbie Basile
(American Lightweight Champ)

Exercise	Sets	Reps
Leg Extensions	3–4	10–15
supersetted with . . .		
Angled Leg Presses	3–4	10–15
Leg Extensions	3–4	10–15
supersetted with . . .		
Sissy Squats	3–4	10–15
Stiff-Leg Deadlifts	3–4	10–15
Standing Leg Curls	3–4	10–15
Lunges	3–4	10–15

Lisa Lyon
(World Champion)

Exercise	Sets	Reps
Squats	4–5	10–12
Leg Presses	4–5	10–12
Leg Extensions	4–5	12–15
supersetted with . . .		
Leg Curls	4–5	12–15

Sue Ann McKean
(Superbowl of Bodybuilding Champ)

Exercise	Sets	Reps
Squats (warm-up)	1–2	15–20
Hack Squats	4–5	10–12
Leg Extensions	4–5	10–12
Front Squats	4–5	10–12
Lunges	2–3	10–12
Lying Leg Curls	4–5	10–12
Stiff-Leg Deadlifts	4–5	10–12
Cable Leg Adductions	2–3	10–12
Cable Leg Abductions	2–3	10–12
Cable Rear Leg Kicks	2–3	10–12

Kay Baxter (left) and Rachel McLish (right).

4
DIAMOND-SHAPED CALVES

While a few women bodybuilders—Kay Baxter and Lori Bowen come immediately to mind—have naturally massive, flaring, and muscular calf development, the calves are difficult for most women to develop. This is primarily because daily, copious walking has toughened these muscles to the point where it takes exceptionally intense training to budge them into growth.

Favorable genetics *do* play a part in championship calf development, but many women bodybuilders have overcome inherently poor calf structure by dint of carefully thought out, very intense training. **Rachel McLish** (twice Miss Olympia and a Pro World Champion) is one woman who has trained her calves unmercifully since she began bodybuilding workouts, bringing them up from virtual pipestems to world-class development. It wasn't easy for Rachel to solve her calf problems, but she persevered and built

an exceptional pair of calves that harmonize well with her thighs and the development of the remainder of her prize-winning physique.

We feel that the primary reason why women bodybuilders fail to develop championship calves is that they neither train the muscle group heavily enough nor with sufficient intensity. You really have to use some heavy iron, but you also must do all of your calf movements in strict form, going all of the way down to a fully stretched position at the bottom of the exercise and all of the way up on your toes at the top of the movement.

If you are an athlete, your calf muscles are vitally important in promoting good sprint speed. In combination with your thigh muscles, your calves can help you to accelerate quickly from a dead stop and reach a very fast sprint speed. Our theory of sports condi-

41

tioning is that a chain is only as strong as its weakest link, so an athlete should take care to strengthen every part of her body, including her calves.

Health- and fitness-minded women should tone and strengthen their calves as well, even though many women abhor the idea of developing bulging calf muscles. But we once did a survey of the male readers of *Muscle & Fitness* magazine, and 92% of them applauded the idea of women possessing muscular calves. We don't think you will ruin the esthetics of your legs by building up your calf muscles; rather, you will improve the overall shape of your legs.

CALF ANATOMY AND KINESIOLOGY

There are two primary muscle groups on the backs of your lower legs—the *gastrocnemius* and *soleus* muscles. The soleus is a wide, flat muscle lying beneath the heart-shaped gastrocnemius. Both muscles contract to extend your feet and toes, but the soleus can only fully contract in this capacity when your leg is bent at at least a 30-degree angle. So, you will primarily stress your gastrocs when you do Standing Toe Raises and your soleus muscles when you perform Seated Toe Raises.

There are several other smaller muscle groups in your lower legs, all of which are developed through various types of Toe Raises. The only exception to this rule is the *tibialis anterior* muscle which runs up the front of your shin and contracts to pull your foot and toes upward, the opposite movement from Toe Raises. Very few bodybuilders discover that they need to do direct exercises for their tibialis anterior muscles, but if you do, you need only place a heavy barbell plate on your toes and flex your feet toward your knees to stress the muscle group.

CALF TRAINING SECRETS

Since the calf muscles are tough, dense tissue, you must train them more frequently than other muscle groups. At least four days per week of calf training is necessary for good progress in developing this muscle group, and many champions train their calves up to six days per week. We personally feel that a three-day calf training cycle is optimum, one heavy day using low reps (8–10 repetitions), one light day using high reps (15–20), and one day of rest. Then the cycle can be repeated beginning with the fourth day and continued *ad infinitum*.

We also firmly believe that you should train your calves using the Weider Muscle Confusion Training Principle, constantly varying the exercises you use, the amount of weight you place on the muscles, the number of sets you perform of each movement, the number of reps you use, and even the length of rest intervals you take between sets. Virtually every top woman bodybuilder who has trained her calves with muscle confusion has reported very good gains to us. Give it a try!

CALF EXERCISES

It's essential that you correctly master each calf exercise described and illustrated in this section. If you don't do the movements correctly, you will receive less than optimum developmental value from them. And since it's very difficult to unlearn bad exercise habits, it's best to learn the exercises correctly from the very start of your involvement in bodybuilding.

Barbell Toe Raises

Emphasis—This basic movement is best used in a home-gym setting when you don't have access to a standing calf machine. Barbell Toe Raises directly stress the gastrocnemius muscles of your calves.

Starting Position—Place a moderately heavy barbell across your shoulders and behind your neck as for a set of Squats. Place your toes and the balls of your feet on a calf block (a block of wood about 4 × 4 inches in width and thickness). Your feet should be set about shoulder-width apart and your toes should be pointed directly forward. Keeping your legs and torso straight, sag your heels as

Barbell Toe Raise—start, left; finish, right.

far below the level of your toes as possible to completely stretch your calves at the bottom point of the movement.

The Movement—Trying as hard as you can to maintain body balance, rise up as high as you can on your toes. Slowly lower yourself back to the starting point and repeat the movement for an appropriate number of repetitions.

Training Tip—You will find it difficult to balance yourself, so this movement is normally best performed on a standing calf machine which eliminates the necessity of fighting for your balance. In a home gym environment, however, it is the best available

exercise other than One-Leg Toe Raises for gastrocnemius development.

Exercise Variations—On all calf exercises, you can change the type of stress placed on your gastrocnemius and/or soleus muscles by placing your feet at different angles as you perform the movements. Do some sets with your toes pointed straight ahead as just described, some with your toes pointed outward at 45-degree angles on each side, and some sets with your toes pointed inward at 45-degree angles. You can also change the stress on your calves somewhat by placing your feet varying distances apart as you do the exercises.

Standing Calf Machine Toe Raise—start, left; finish, right.

Standing Calf Machine Toe Raises

Emphasis—As with Barbell Toe Raises, Standing Calf Machine Toe Raises directly stress the gastrocnemius muscles in relative isolation from the rest of your body. Secondary stress is on your soleus muscles.

Starting Position—Step up to a standing calf machine and bend your knees sufficiently to allow you to position your shoulders comfortably beneath the yokes of the machine. Next, place the balls of your feet and your toes on the calf block, your feet set about shoulder-width apart and your toes pointed directly forward. Finally, straighten your body to bear the weight of the machine and sag your heels as far below the level of your toes as possible to pre-stretch your calf muscles at the start of the movement.

The Movement—Rise up as high as you can on your toes, hold this peak contracted top position of the exercise for a moment, then return to the starting point. Repeat the movement for the suggested number of repetitions.

Exercise Variations—You can vary your foot angles and the width of your foot placement on the toe block to subject your calves to different stresses. And, Rachel McLish occasionally likes to do this exercise with one leg at a time.

Seated Calf Machine Toe Raises

Emphasis—Since this movement is performed with your legs bent at 90-degree angles, it is perfect for completely contracting the soleus muscles. Secondary stress is on your gastrocnemius muscles as you perform Seated Calf Machine Toe Raises.

Starting Position—Chances are good that you will need to adjust the height of the knee pads on this machine before you do the movement. You can make this adjustment by removing a pin in the tubular column of metal that attaches the pads to the lever arm of the machine, lengthening or shortening the attachment member, and replacing the pin. Sit on the machine seat and place your toes and the balls of your feet on the toe piece of the apparatus. Sag your heels down far enough so you can pull the pads over your knees. Push down on your toes and move the stop bar of the machine forward to release the weight. Again, sag your heels as far below the level of your toes as possible.

The Movement—Extend your feet as completely as possible to rise up on your toes under heavy resistance. Lower slowly back to the starting point and repeat the movement.

Exercise Variations—You should be sure to play with the width of your foot placement on the toe member of the machine, as well as with the angles at which you place your toes. If you train in a home gym without the benefit of a seated calf machine, you can improvise this movement by padding the center of a heavy barbell with a thick towel, sitting at the end of a flat exercise bench with your toes on a calf block, and having a training partner lift the weight up to rest across your knees so you can do the exercise.

Seated Calf Machine Toe Raise—start, left; finish, right.

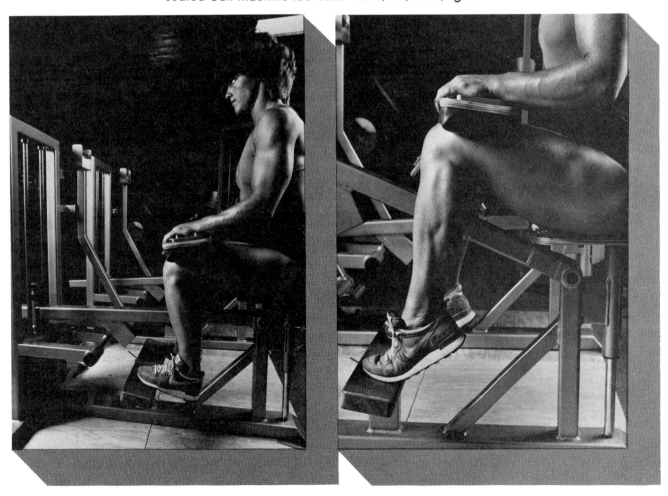

Calf Presses

Emphasis—Calf Presses are a very comfortable way to directly stress your gastrocnemius muscles. Secondary stress is on your soleus muscles.

Starting Position—You can perform this movement on a 45-degree-angled leg press machine, a vertical leg press machine, a Nautilus leg press machine. We will describe performance of Calf Presses on the 45-degree machine, and you can easily extrapolate this explanation to the other machines, should you have access to and wish to use one of them. Sit in the machine with your back resting against the back pad and place only the balls of your feet and your toes about shoulder-width apart on the sliding platform of the machine. Simply press your legs straight, and don't bother to release the weight by rotating the stop bars because the range of movement in this exercise won't require this. Allow your toes to travel as far toward you as possible while keeping your legs straight in order to fully stretch your calves.

The Movement—Slowly extend your feet and toes as completely as possible, pause in this peak contracted position for a moment, and return to the starting point. Repeat the exercise for the required number of repetitions.

Training Tip—You can do an interesting type of negative rep movement on this machine. Simply push the weight out with both feet, then lower it down with only your left foot and resist it with the strength of your left calf. Push it out again with both feet and lower it the next time with your right foot. Continue alternating feet in this manner until you have fully fatigued your calves.

Calf Press (on 45-degree-angled machine)—start, top right; finish, bottom right.

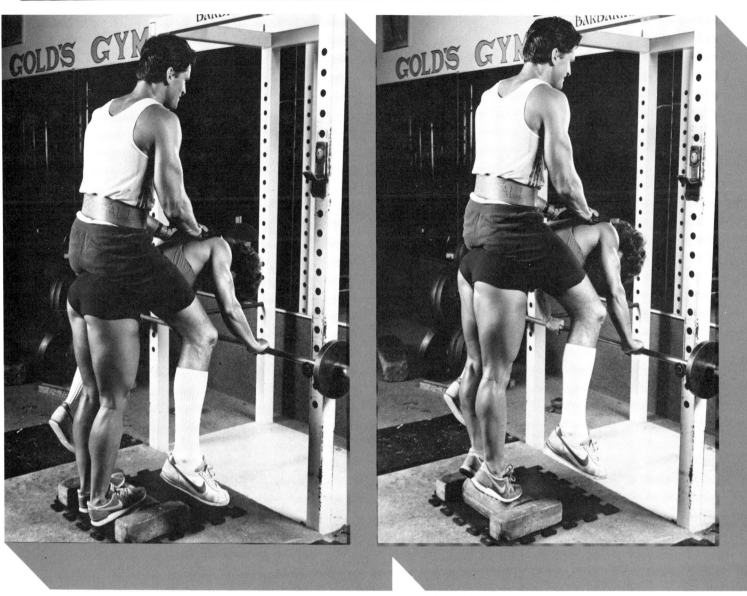

Donkey Toe Raise—start, left; finish, right.

Donkey Toe Raises

Emphasis—This odd-appearing exercise is excellent for intensely stressing your gastrocnemius muscles. Strong secondary stress is on your soleus muscles.

Starting Position—Stand with the balls of your feet and your toes on a calf block and bend over to rest your hands on a flat exercise bench in a position that puts your torso parallel to the floor when your legs are held straight. Alternatively, you can rest your head and forearms on the flat surface of a leg extension machine or similar apparatus. Have a heavy training partner jump up astride your hips and balance himself/herself in place as though riding a horse. Sag your heels as far below the level of your toes as possible to prestretch your calves for the exercise.

The Movement—Rise up as high as you can on your toes, hold the peak contracted top position for a moment, and return slowly to the starting point. Repeat the movement for the desired number of repetitions.

Exercise Variations—You should experiment with different widths of foot placement, as well as with the angle at which you set each foot on the calf block in order to stress different sections of your calf muscles.

One-Leg Toe Raise at finish.

One-Leg Toe Raises

Emphasis—This is a very good movement for building up your gastrocnemius muscles. Since they require such a minimum amount of equipment, One-Leg Toe Raises are excellent for home-gym use.

Starting Position—Grasp a moderately weighted dumbbell in your left hand and stand with the ball of your left foot and your toes on a calf block. Use your right hand to balance your body as you do the movement by grasping a sturdy upright, but refrain from pulling up on your support to assist your fatigued calf muscles during the movement. Curl your right leg up until your right shin is parallel to the floor where it will not be involved in the exercise. Relax your left calf muscle and sag your heel as far below the level of your toes as possible.

The Movement—Rise up as high as you can on your toes, hold this peak contracted top position for a moment, and slowly return to the starting point. Repeat the exercise for the suggested number of repetitions. Be sure to perform an equal number of sets and repetitions for each leg.

Exercise Variations—You'll find it difficult to do this movement with your foot angled inward, but you'll be able to perform it easily with your toes pointed straight ahead or angled slightly outward.

SUGGESTED CALF ROUTINES

While this book is intended primarily for intermediate and advanced weight trainers and bodybuilders, there may be a few beginning-level women reading this chapter. We define a beginner as any woman with less than six to eight weeks of training experience behind her. Following is a beginning-level calf program that can be used three nonconsecutive days per week:

Exercise	Sets	Reps
Standing Calf Machine Toe Raises	2	12–15
Seated Calf Machine Toe Raises	1–2	10–12

After you have completed six to eight weeks of the foregoing program you can move up to the following low-intermediate routine, which can also be performed three nonconsecutive days per week:

Exercise	Sets	Reps
Calf Presses	3	15–20
Donkey Toe Raises	2	12–15

Another six to eight weeks of training will bring you to the full intermediate level of training. At that point you can use the following calf routine four days per week:

Mon–Thu

Exercise	Sets	Reps
Seated Calf Machine Toe Raises	4	8–10
Calf Presses	4	12–15

Tue–Fri

Exercise	Sets	Reps
Standing Calf Machine Toe Raises	3	15–20
One-Leg Toe Raises	3	15–20

Gail Schroeder.

The 1980 Olympia posedown: (left to right) Stacey Bentley, Corrine Machado-Ching, Lynn Conkwright, Rachel McLish, and Aubey Paulik.

CALF ROUTINES OF THE CHAMPIONS

It's important to understand that the routines presented in this section are of extremely high intensity. If you have less than a year of solid, all-out training behind you, you won't make good gains using any of these programs. And it's likely that you will soon overtrain using one of these routines, which can even lead to a regression in your physical development. However, by scaling these routines down to your own ability levels, you can make good progress on them. Simply do the same exercises as your favorite champion, but perform fewer sets of each movement.

Laura Combes
(American Champion)

Day One

Exercise	Sets	Reps
Seated Calf Raises	5-8	10-12
Nautilus Calf Presses	3-5	10-15

Day Two

Exercise	Sets	Reps
Standing Calf Raises	3-5	15-20

Day Three

(Rest)

Lisa Elliott-Kolakowski
(Gold's Classic Champion)

Mon-Thu

Exercise	Sets	Reps
Standing Calf Raises	4-5	15
Donkey Calf Raises	4-5	15
One-Leg Toe Raises	2-3	20

Tue-Fri

Exercise	Sets	Reps
Seated Calf Raises	3-4	10
Calf Presses	2-3	15

Kike Elomaa
(Miss Olympia)

Exercise	Sets	Reps
Seated Calf Raises	4	15
Standing Calf Raises	4	15
Calf Presses (Nautilus)	4	15

Stella Martinez
(Ms. USA)

Day One

Exercise	Sets	Reps
Donkey Calf Raises	5	15-20
Seated Calf Raises	3-5	10-15

Day Two

Exercise	Sets	Reps
Standing Calf Raises	4	12-15
One Leg Calf Raises	2-3	15-20

Sue Ann McKean
(Superbowl of Bodybuilding Champion)

Tue-Fri

Exercise	Sets	Reps
Seated Calf Raises	5-8	12-15
Standing Calf Raises	5-8	15-20

Wed-Sat

Exercise	Sets	Reps
Calf Presses	3-5	20-25

Lesley Koslow
(Ms. Florida)

Mon-Thu

Exercise	Sets	Reps
Standing Calf Raises	4	10-12
Seated Calf Raises	3	12-15
Calf Presses	2	15-20

Tue-Fri

Exercise	Sets	Reps
Donkey Calf Raises	3	15-20
One-Leg Toe Raises	2	15-20

Corinne Machado-Ching and Shelley Gruwell (forward right).

5
BREATHTAKING BACKS

It seems that virtually any woman bodybuilder who is willing to follow a strict diet can develop a very muscular-appearing back for display onstage at a competition, but very few have been able to build significant thickness in their back muscles. Notable exceptions are Tina Plakinger (Ms. America), Carla Dunlap (Miss Olympia), and Bev Francis (world record-holding powerlifter turned bodybuilder). Tina, Carla, and Bev all possess very deep back development in addition to startling back muscularity.

If you are a competitive bodybuilder, you should attempt to develop both width and thickness in your back, the width coming from fully developed latissimus dorsi muscles and the thickness from complete development of all the many back muscles. So once you have dieted down to contest condition your back will be so fully developed and ripped to shreds that you'll easily defeat women who have failed to pay sufficient attention to training their backs.

You can always spot lazy bodybuilders onstage because they invariably have underdeveloped backs and thighs. Since the back and thigh muscles are the largest in your body, it's a relatively painful process to train them at peak intensity. During a hard set of leg or back work you'll get a massive and painful buildup of fatigue toxins, and after the set you'll pant for two or three minutes to repay your oxygen debt. As a result, women who are unwilling to work hard just go through the motions when training their thighs and back, and their physiques are woefully weak in these two areas.

Athletes also need powerful back development because the back muscles are significantly involved in most sports, either directly or in a supporting role while other muscles carry the load. Our theory in sports conditioning is that a chain is only as strong as its weakest link, so an athlete should take care to strengthen every part of her body.

The health- and fitness-minded woman should strengthen her back in order to avoid becoming one of the millions of individuals who incur lower back injuries each year. You can avoid many back injuries by simply paying attention to strengthening the erector spinae muscles of your lower back.

BACK ANATOMY AND KINESIOLOGY

There are three main muscle groups in your back—the trapezius muscles of your upper back, the latissimus dorsi group of your mid-back, and the erector spinae muscles of your lower back. Of course, there are several other smaller groups, but they will be completely developed if you merely pay close attention to including exercises for each of the three main back muscle groups in your training programs.

The trapezius is a large, kite-shaped muscle with the top point at the base of your skull, the two side points near your shoulder joints, and the lower point roughly halfway down your spinal column. Although many bodybuilders consider the trapezius to be a shoulder muscle, it actually is the largest muscle group of the upper back. Still, it does contract to move the shoulders, usually both upward and backward. The traps also contract to help force the shoulder blades toward each other.

The large latissimus dorsi muscles lie across the middle section of your back on each side, and in a well-developed woman bodybuilder this back muscle gives a V shape to the torso when viewed from either the front or the back. The latissimus dorsi originates primarily from attachments along the spine and inserts with a large tendon to the humerus (upper arm bone) on each side of your body. The latissimus dorsi muscles contract to pull your upper arms downward and backward.

The erector spinae muscles of your lower back lie like two thick columns of muscle on either side of your spinal column. Although

the spinal erectors run from the base of your pelvis almost the full length of your spine, they are most easily visible from the middle of your back to the lowest part of your back. Your erector spinae muscles contract to move your torso from a position bent forward in relation to your legs to a position in which your entire body is straight. Your erectors also contract to help arch your back as well as to stabilize your torso in an upright position when you are standing, walking, or running.

BACK TRAINING SECRETS

Developing your traps and erectors is a fairly straightforward proposition, but there are several secrets that you should understand in order to develop your lats fully. The first of these secrets is that you can fully contract your lats only when you have your back arched. Therefore, you must be careful always to arch your back in the finish position of all of your lat exercises. On some exercises, such as Chins and Lat Machine Pulldowns, you can keep your back arched throughout the movement. On others, such as Seated Pulley Rows, you will begin the movement with your back rounded and finish the exercise with your back arched.

Secondly, you can work for either lat thickness or lat width according to which exercises you choose to perform. Movements in which your elbows travel predominantly downward (e.g., Chins and Lat Pulldowns) primarily develop width in your lats, while exercises in which your elbows primarily travel in an arc perpendicular to the downward movement just described (e.g., Barbell Rows and Dumbbell Rows) build thickness in your lats. However, there is one exercise (Seated Pulley Rows) that allows you to build both width and thickness simultaneously in your latissimus dorsi muscles.

Finally, all Pullover movements that are normally performed to stress the pectoral muscles of your chest are also excellent for lat development. These movements include Nautilus Pullovers, Cross-Bench Dumbbell Pullovers, Stiff-Arm Pullovers, and Bent-Arm

Pullovers. So, when you are performing a split routine in which you stress your chest and back in one workout, you will find it valuable to perform some type of Pullovers as a transitional movement between the two body parts. For example, if you hit your chest first and your back second in a workout, finish up your chest workout with several sets of Pullovers to tune up your back muscles for the heavy training they will soon receive.

BACK EXERCISES

It's essential that you correctly master each back exercise described and illustrated in this section. If you don't do the movements correctly, you will receive less than optimum developmental value from them. And since it's very difficult to unlearn bad exercise habits, it's best to learn the exercises correctly from the very start.

Upright Rows

Emphasis—This is one of the best single exercises for the muscles of your shoulder girdle. Primary emphasis is placed on your trapezius and deltoids, while secondary stress is placed on your biceps, brachialis, and the gripping muscles of your forearms.

Starting Position—Take a narrow overgrip in the middle of a barbell handle (there should be about six inches of space showing between your index fingers). Set your feet about shoulder width apart and stand erect with your arms straight down at your sides and your hands and the barbell resting across your upper thighs.

The Movement—Being sure to keep your elbows well above the level of your hands at all times, slowly pull the barbell directly upward from the starting position until your hands touch the underside of your chin. At this top position, rotate your shoulders backward and squeeze your shoulder blades together for a moment. Slowly lower the barbell down to the starting point and repeat the movement for the suggested number of repetitions.

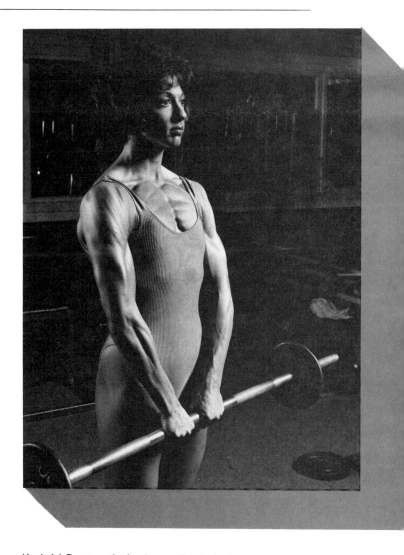

Upright Rows—start, above; finish, below.

Tina Plakinger uses a short bar and pulley to perform Upright Rows.

Barbell Shrugs—start, below; finish, bottom.

Training Tips—A very similar movement can be performed by attaching a short bar handle to a floor pulley. Or you can perform a somewhat similar exercise by holding two dumbbells in your hands.

Shoulder Shrugs

Emphasis—All variations of Shrugs stress the trapezius muscles with great intensity. Secondary stress is placed on the gripping muscles of the forearms.

Starting Position—Take a shoulder width overgrip on a moderately heavy barbell. Set your feet about shoulder width apart and stand erect with your arms running straight down at your sides and the barbell resting across your upper thighs. It's essential throughout this exercise that you keep your arms straight. Think of your arms merely as cables running from the weight to your shoulders.

Using dumbbells you can perform Rotating Shoulder Shrugs—start, left; upward position, right; backward position, below.

The Movement—Sag your shoulders downward and forward as far as is comfortably possible, then shrug them upward and to the rear as high as you can. Slowly lower back to the bottom position and repeat the movement.

Training Tips—A very similar movement can be performed standing between the handles of the bench press station of a Universal Gym machine, grasping the pressing handles to provide resistance. If you are less than about 5′6″ tall, however, you may need to stand on a thick block of wood in order to get a good stretch in the bottom position of Machine Shrugs. A second common variation is performed while holding two moderately heavy dumbbells in your hands. With Dumbbell Shrugs you can actually shrug your shoulders upward and downward in a rotating manner, a movement that is called Rotating Shoulder Shrugs.

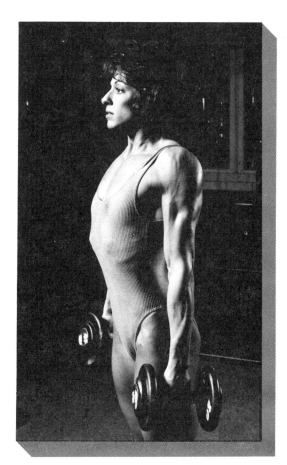

Deadlift—start, left; midpoint, below left;
finish, below right.

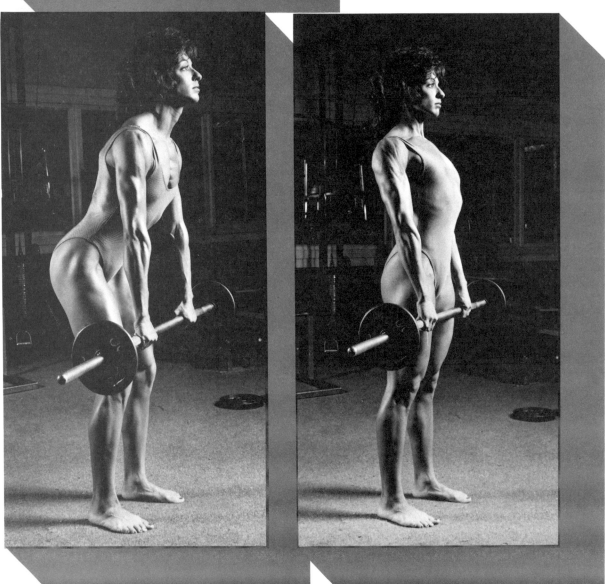

Deadlifts

Emphasis—This is one of the best power-building exercises in existence. Deadlifts strongly stress your erectors, quadriceps, buttocks, hips, and the gripping muscles of your forearms. Secondary stress is placed on your trapezius and other back muscles, as well as on your hamstrings and abdominal muscles.

Starting Position—Stand with your shins touching the bar of a moderately heavy barbell, your feet set about shoulder width apart. Take an overgrip on the barbell with your hands set slightly wider than your shoulders on each side. Keeping your arms straight, bend your legs and flatten your back to assume a position in which your hips are above your knees and your shoulders are above the level of your hips. Look either straight ahead or slightly upward.

The Movement—Slowly pull the barbell off the floor by first straightening your legs and then following through by straightening your torso until your body is completely erect. Pull your shoulders back, then lower the bar back to the starting point by reversing the process used to raise the bar. Repeat.

Training Tips—If you have trouble gripping the bar when using maximum weights, you can use a reversed grip in which one palm is facing forward and the other is facing the rear. This will make your grip on the bar much more secure when doing limit Deadlifts (i.e., when you use maximum weights for only one or two reps). Incidentally, you should avoid doing limit single attempts in this lift because it becomes relatively easy to injure yourself when you do so. It's best to do sets of about five repetitions when doing Deadlifts.

Stiff-Leg Deadlifts

Emphasis—This variation of the Deadlift places maximum stress on your spinal erectors, buttocks, and the hamstrings at the back of your thighs. Indeed, Stiff-Leg Deadlifts are just as effective a thigh biceps exercise as Leg Curls. Secondary stress is placed on your upper back and forearm muscle groups.

Starting Position—Place a moderately weighted barbell across a flat exercise bench. Stand on the exercise bench with your feet about six inches apart and take a shoulder-width overgrip on the barbell handle. With your legs bent, lift the weight up to your thighs and straighten your entire body. Be sure to keep your arms and legs held straight as you do Stiff-Leg Deadlifts.

The Movement—Keeping your back as flat as possible, slowly bend over at the waist and lower the barbell downward as far as you comfortably can. Ideally, you'll be able to touch the bar to your toes comfortably. Slowly recover to the starting position and repeat the movement. Since your lower back is in a relatively weak mechanical position when your legs are held straight, it's essential that you do this movement slowly and with no abrupt jerks along its range of motion.

Training Tips—You could perform Stiff-Leg

Stiff-Leg Deadlift at finish.

Deadlifts standing on the floor, but the diameter of the plates on the barbell would terminate the movement well short of its potential range of motion. Therefore, you should always do Stiff-Leg Deadlifts while standing on an exercise bench or a thick block of wood.

Hyperextensions

Emphasis—Hyperextensions will strongly stress your spinal erectors, buttocks, and hamstrings. Secondary stress is placed on the muscles of your upper back.

Starting Position—Stand in the middle of a hyperextension bench, facing toward the large flat pad attached to the apparatus. Lean forward and place your pelvic structure on the pad, allowing your heels to come to rest beneath the pads at the rear of the apparatus. Slide your pelvis forward far enough so you can comfortably flex your body at the waist, then flex forward until your torso is hanging down perpendicular to the floor. Keep your legs straight during the movement and hold your hands behind your head and neck as you do the exercise.

The Movement—Slowly arch your back and bring your head and shoulders upward until your torso is slightly above an imaginary line drawn parallel to the floor. Be sure not to arch up any higher than this, though it's easily possible to do so, because arching up too high can place a compression stress on your spinal vertebrae. Lower back to the starting point and repeat the movement.

Training Tips—If you don't have a hyperextension bench handy, you can simply lie with your legs across a table or high exercise bench and have a training partner restrain your legs. With either variation of Hyperextensions, you can add resistance to the exercise by holding a loose barbell plate behind your head.

Hyperextensions—start, left; finish, right.

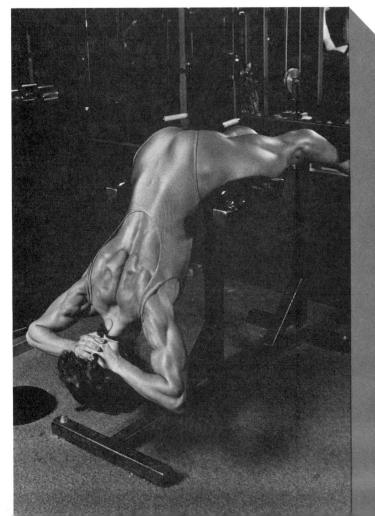

Good Mornings—start, left; finish, right.

Good Mornings

Emphasis—Good Mornings strongly stress your spinal erectors, buttocks, and hamstrings. Secondary emphasis is placed on the muscles of your upper back.

Starting Position—Place a light barbell across your shoulders behind your neck and balance it in position during the movement by grasping the bar out near the plates. Position your feet about shoulder width apart, stand erect, and keep your legs straight throughout the movement.

The Movement—Slowly bend forward until your torso is slightly below an imaginary line drawn parallel to the floor. Return slowly to the starting point and repeat the movement for the suggested number of repetitions.

Training Tips—If the bar cuts painfully into your neck, you should pad it by wrapping a towel around the barbell bar. With slightly heavier weights you can do a similar movement with your legs bent a few degrees.

Barbell Bent Rows

Emphasis—This movement is one of the best all-around upper-body exercises in existence. Barbell Bent Rows strongly stress the latissimus dorsi, trapezius, biceps, brachialis, and posterior deltoid muscles. Secondary stress is placed on the erector spinae and the gripping muscles of your forearms.

Starting Position—Take a shoulder-width overgrip on a barbell lying at your feet. Straighten your arms and flatten your back. With your knees slightly unlocked, raise your torso up until it is parallel to the floor.

The Movement—Keeping your elbows in close to your sides, slowly bend your arms and pull the barbell upward to touch your lower rib cage. Lower the weight back to the starting point and repeat the movement.

Training Tips—If you use large-diameter plates, they won't be clear of the floor in the correct starting position unless you do your Barbell Bent Rows standing on a thick block of wood or flat exercise bench. You can vary the width of your grip on the bar from one as narrow as with your hands touching in the middle of the bar to one as wide as the length of the barbell bar will permit.

Barbell Bent Rows—start, left; finish, right.

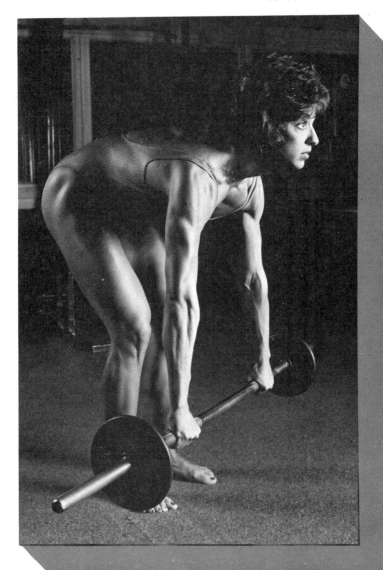

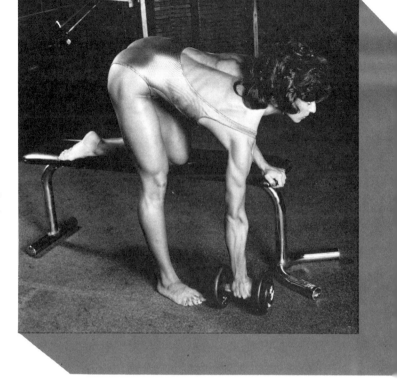

Dumbbell Bent Rows—start, above; finish, below.

Dumbbell Bent Rows

Emphasis—As with the barbell version of this movement, Dumbbell Bent Rows place strong stress on the latissimus dorsi, trapezius, biceps, brachialis, and posterior deltoid muscles. Secondary stress is placed on the gripping muscles of the forearms.

Starting Point—Place a moderately heavy dumbbell on the floor on the left side of a flat exercise bench. Kneel with your right knee on the bench and your right hand a bit forward of your knee to brace your torso in a position parallel to the floor. Your left foot should be placed somewhat to the rear. Grasp the dumbbell in your left hand, fully straighten your left arm, and rotate your left shoulder slightly toward the floor to stretch the back muscles fully on the left side of your body.

The Movement—Keeping your elbow in at your side, slowly pull the dumbbell directly upward until it touches the side of your torso. You should rotate your left shoulder backward a bit in order to contract your back muscles fully. Slowly lower the weight back to the fully stretched position and repeat the movement.

Training Tips—You can also do this exercise with two dumbbells at one time. Simply assume the same position as for Barbell Bent Rows, but use two dumbbells rather than the barbell.

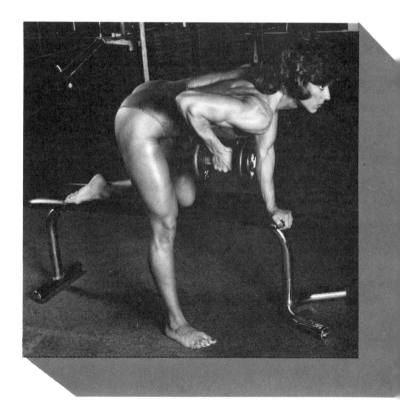

Seated Pulley Rows

Emphasis—This is one of the best all-around latissimus dorsi movements in that it builds both width and thickness in the muscle group. Significant stress is also placed on the spinal erectors, trapezius, biceps, brachialis, and forearm muscles.

Starting Position—Attach a handle that gives you a narrow parallel grip to the end of a cable running through a floor pulley. Grasp the handle with your palms toward each other, place your feet against the restraint bar at the front end of the rowing machine seat, and sit down on the seat. Your legs should be kept slightly unlocked throughout your set. Lean forward as far as you can at the waist and straighten your arms to stretch your lats completely.

The Movement—Simultaneously pull the handle in to touch your lower rib cage and sit erect. As you pull the handle toward your body, be sure to keep your elbows in close to the sides of your body. And don't allow your torso to move farther back than a position perpendicular to the floor. Be sure to arch your back as you pull the handle in to touch your torso, then return the handle to the starting point and repeat the movement for the required number of repetitions.

Training Tips—Most bodybuilders do this movement with a low pulley mounted only about a foot from the floor, but it can also be performed effectively with a high pulley mounted five or six feet above floor level. Regardless of the height of the pulley, you can also do this movement with a straight bar handle or with the handle that allows you a shoulder-width parallel grip.

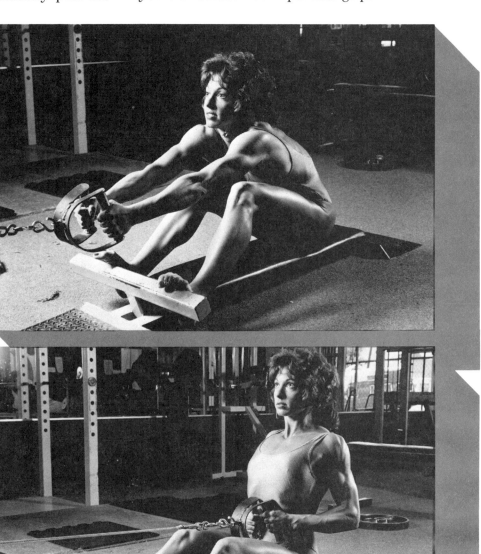

Seated Pulley Rows—start,
top; finish, bottom.

T-Bar Rows—start, left; finish, right.

T-Bar Rows

Emphasis—T-Bar Rows place primary emphasis on the lats, spinal erectors, traps, posterior deltoids, biceps, brachialis, and forearm muscles.

Starting Position—Stand on the platforms on each side of the T-bar. Slightly bend your legs and keep them bent throughout the movement to reduce potentially harmful stress on your lower back. Bend over and grasp the handles attached to the bar. Completely straighten your arms and raise your torso upward until it is parallel to the floor. Arch your back.

The Movement—Use lat and arm strength to pull the T-bar up to touch your chest. As you are pulling the bar upward, don't allow your head and torso to come upward along with it. Slowly lower the bar back to the starting point and repeat the movement.

Training Tips—Most T-bar machines are plate-loading, but there is a machine that works via a cable running through a pulley to a weight stack. This T-bar apparatus allows a much longer range of motion than the plate-loaded machine, so it should be used whenever possible. And if you use the plate-loading machine, try to use plates of the smallest possible diameter in order to encourage a longer range of motion.

Chins

Emphasis—All variations of Chins place intense stress on the lats, posterior deltoids, brachialis, and biceps muscles. Secondary stress is placed on the forearms and other upper back muscles.

Starting Position—Jump up to grasp the bar with an overgrip, your hands set two or three inches wider on each side than your shoulders. Bend your legs and cross your ankles. Completely straighten your arms and stretch your lats.

The Movement—Being sure to keep your elbows back and your back arched, bend your arms and slowly pull your body upward until your chin is above the bar. If possible, pull yourself up high enough to touch the bar to your upper chest. Slowly lower yourself back to the starting point and repeat the movement for an appropriate number of reps. This movement is called a Front Chin, and it places greater stress on the lower lats than on any other part of your latissimus dorsi group.

Training Tips—You can also do Chins behind Neck in which you pull yourself up to touch the bar on your upper trapezius in back of your neck. Chins behind Neck place greater stress on your upper lats. With both types of Chins you can vary the width of your grip inward until your hands are actually touching or outward as far as the length of the chinning bar will allow. Finally, you can also use an undergrip on the bar for your Chins, a grip that puts your biceps in a very strong pulling position.

Chins—start, left; finish (behind neck), center; finish (in front of neck), right.

Lat Machine Pulldowns—start, left; finish, right.

Lat Machine Pulldowns

Emphasis—All variations of Pulldowns place intense stress on the lats, posterior deltoids, brachialis, and biceps muscles. Secondary stress is placed on the forearms and other upper back muscles.

Starting Position—Most large gyms have lat machines with special seats that help hold your body in position as you do the movement. If you don't have such a seat, you will need to sit or kneel on the gym floor beneath the pulley and have a training partner restrain your body by pushing downward on your shoulders. With the seat arrangements, take an overgrip on the lat bar with your hands set three or four inches wider than your shoulders on each side. Sit on the seat, wedge your knees beneath the restraint bar, fully straighten your arms, and arch your back.

The Movement—Being sure to keep your back arched and your elbows back throughout the movement, use lat and arm strength to pull the bar down to touch the upper part of your chest. Slowly return the bar to the starting point and repeat the movement. This exercise is called a Front Lat Pulldown movement. You can also do Pulldowns behind Neck.

Training Tips—There are a variety of handles that you can attach to a lat machine cable. Normally a straight bar handle about three feet long is used, but a long angled bar is frequently used on a lat machine. You can also use a handle that provides you with a shoulder-width grip, placing your palms toward each other, as well as a handle that

Lat Pulldown with narrow, parallel grip.

gives you a parallel grip like this but with your hands close together. With most of these handles you can vary the width of your grip as when performing Chins.

Nautilus Pullovers

Emphasis—Pullovers performed on a Nautilus machine place far more stress on the lats than other variations of the Pullover movement. Significant stress is also placed on the pectorals, serratus, and those upper back muscles that rotate the scapulae.

Starting Position—Adjust the height of the seat so it places your shoulder joints on the same level as the pivot points of the machine when you are sitting in the seat. Sit in the seat, secure the seat belt over your lap, and place your feet on the foot pedal in front of you. Push down on the pedal with leg strength to bring the padded parts of the lever arm forward far enough so you can position your elbows against the pads and lightly grasp the crossarm connecting the two pads. Slowly release the pedal to assume the full weight of the apparatus, then allow the machine's resistance to pull your elbows as far upward and to the rear in a semicircular arc as is comfortably possible.

The Movement—Use lat strength to push with your elbows against the pads, which will move them forward and downward in a semicircular arc until the crossbar connecting the lever arms contacts your abdomen. Hold this position for a moment and slowly return to the starting point. Repeat the movement for the desired number of repetitions.

Training Tips—To intensify the peak contraction effect of this movement, you can do several burns in the bottom position of the exercise once you have approached failure on the full movement.

Nautilus Pullovers—start, left; finish, below.

SUGGESTED BACK ROUTINES

While this book is intended primarily for intermediate and advanced weight trainers and bodybuilders, there may be a few beginners reading this chapter. We define a beginner as any woman with less than six to eight weeks of training experience behind her. Following is a beginning-level back program that can be used on three nonconsecutive days per week:

Exercise	Sets	Reps
Barbell Bent Rows	3	8–12
Front Lat Pulldowns	2	8–12

After you have completed six to eight weeks of the foregoing program you can move up to the following low-intermediate routine, which you can perform on three nonconsecutive days per week:

Exercise	Sets	Reps
Hyperextensions	2	10–15
Barbell Shrugs	2	10–15
Seated Pulley Rows	3	8–12
Pulldowns behind Neck	3	8–12
Nautilus Pullovers	1–2	8–12

Another six to eight weeks of training will bring you to the full intermediate level of training. At that point, you can use the following back routine on three nonconsecutive days per week:

Exercise	Sets	Reps
Pulley Upright Rows	3	8–12
Stiff-Leg Deadlifts	3	10–15
One-Arm Dumbbell Bent Rows	3	8–12
Pulldowns behind Neck	3	8–12
Seated Pulley Rows	2–3	8–12

Advanced bodybuilders during off-season workouts normally follow a four-day split routine (see Chapter 10) in which they train half of their bodies on Mondays and Thursdays and the other half on Tuesdays and Fridays. Therefore, they train the back only twice per week, which allows them to place much greater stress on the body part. Following is a sample off-season training program that can be used two days per week:

Exercise	Sets	Reps
Rotating Dumbbell Shrugs	3–4	10–15
Hyperextensions	3–4	10–15
Front Chins	3	max
T-Bar Rows	3	8–12
Pulldowns behind Neck	2–3	8–12
Nautilus Pullovers	2–3	8–12

BACK ROUTINES OF THE CHAMPIONS

It's important to understand that the routines presented in this section are of extremely high intensity. If you have less than a year of solid, all-out training behind you, you won't make gains using any of these programs. And it's likely that you will soon overtrain using one of these routines, which can even lead to a regression in your physical development. However, by scaling these routines down to your own ability levels, you *can* make good progress with them. Simply do the same exercises as your favorite champion, but perform fewer sets of each movement.

Carla Dunlap
(Miss Olympia)

Exercise	Sets	Reps
Close-Grip Lat Pulldowns (warm-up)	4	8–10
Barbell Bent Rows (wide grip)	4	8–10
Bent Laterals	4	8–10
Seated Pulley Rows	4	8–10
Dumbbell Bent Rows	4	8–10
Deadlifts	4	6–8
Dumbbell Shrugs	4	10–12

Stacey Bentley
(Zane Pro Invitational Champion)

Exercise	Sets	Reps
Deadlifts	5	12–15
Dumbbell Bent Rows	5	12–15
Hyperextensions	5	12–15
Front Pulldowns	3	6–8
Seated Pulley Rows	3–5	8–12

Sue Ann McKean
(Superbowl of Bodybuilding Champ)

Exercise	Sets	Reps
Pulley Upright Rows	5	10-12
Dumbbell Stiff-Leg Deadlifts	5-8	10-15
Front Chins	5-8	10-12
Dumbbell Bent Rows	4-5	8-10
Pulldowns behind Neck	4-5	8-10
Stiff-Arm Pulldowns	2-3	10-15

Candy Csencsits
(Miss Olympia Runner-Up)

Exercise	Sets	Reps
Dumbbell Bent Rows	3	8-10
Pulldowns behind Neck	3	8-10
Seated Pulley Rows	3	8-10
Upright Rows	3	8-10
Hyperextensions	3	12-15

Cory Everson
(North American Champion)

Exercise	Sets	Reps
Pulldowns behind Neck	5	10-15
Close-Grip Pulldowns	5	10-15
Hyperextensions	5	15-20

Claudia Wilbourn
(California Champion)

Exercise	Sets	Reps
Front Lat Pulldowns	3	6-10
Seated Pulley Rows	3	6-10
One-Arm Dumbbell Bent Rows	3	6-10
Barbell Shrugs	3	8
One-Arm Low Pulley Rows	3	8

Laura Combes
(American Champion)

Exercise	Sets	Reps
Barbell Shrugs	4-5	10-15
Stiff-Leg Deadlifts	4-5	10-15
Barbell Bent Rows	5	8-10
Front Chins	5	8-10
Seated Pulley Rows	3-4	8-10
Pulldowns behind Neck	3-4	8-10

Stacey Bentley.

Mary Roberts, 1981 Lightweight American Champion.

6
BLASTING THE BUSTLINE

Most women—bodybuilders and normally sedentary women alike—do resistance exercises for their chest muscles. Ordinary women do chest movements with weights and other resistance apparatus in an effort to firm up their bustlines and perhaps improve the shape and contour of their bustlines. And although this practice is widely recommended, it does little if anything to change the appearance of a woman's bustline.

Through bodybuilding training, however, you can develop thick, striated pectorals that will help you win many major bodybuilding championships. Most women bodybuilders are able to develop exceptional pectoral mass and muscularity, but several notable women have taken chest muscle development to new heights. Chief among these are Carla Dunlap (Miss Olympia), Laura Combes (Ms. America), and Bev Francis (world record–holding powerlifter turned bodybuilder).

If you are a competitive bodybuilder, you should attempt to develop balanced thickness in your chest muscle complex. Your pectorals should be uniformly thick from top to bottom and from one side to the other, even though much of your pectoral mass will be covered by your breasts. And you should endeavor to carve the ultimate degree of muscular cuts into your pecs, resulting in a thick and ripped-up chest development.

Athletes in other sports also need powerful chest development because the chest muscles are significantly involved in most sports activities, either directly or in a supporting role while other muscles carry the load. Our theory in championship sports conditioning is that a chain is only as strong as its weakest link, so an athlete should take care to strengthen every part of her body if she's serious about her sport.

Health- and fitness-minded women should work to tone and strengthen their chest

73

muscles in order to present an overall appearance of strength and vitality. As with training for athletic conditioning, you can't allow one part of your body to be significantly underdeveloped if you wish to appear strong and healthy.

CHEST ANATOMY AND KINESIOLOGY

The pectoralis muscle is a large, flat, fan-shaped body of muscle tissue covering your entire upper rib cage. It originates from attachments along your sternum (breast bone), clavicles (collarbones), and ribs, and it inserts on each side of your body via a large tendon through your shoulder joint to your humerus (upper arm bone).

The primary function of your pectoral muscles is to pull your upper arms from a position behind your torso forward and inward toward each other (even actually across each other) in front of your torso. However, you can vary the specific part of your pectoral muscle stressed by an exercise by changing how you pull your upper arms forward.

To begin with, you will find that the first part of this forward-arms movement stresses primarily the outer section of your pecs, while the final part of the movement puts most of the stress on your inner pecs where they attach to your sternum. So, by doing Dumbbell Flyes, you are stressing your outer pecs; and by performing Pec Deck Flyes, you are stressing primarily your inner pecs.

When doing Bench Presses and Flyes, you will lie on one of three benches: a flat exercise bench, an incline exercise bench (angled, with your head at the upper end of the bench), or a decline bench (angled, but with your head at the lower end of the bench). The flat-bench movements place stress on your entire pectoral muscle complex, while incline exercises stress the upper pecs more and decline movements work your lower pectorals with greater intensity.

Many women also consider the serratus muscles (fingerlike projections over the upper ribs on each side) as part of their chest muscle complex. The serratus muscles contract to depress your rib cage, and you can hit them most effectively in a bodybuilding workout by performing various kinds of Pullover movements.

CHEST TRAINING SECRETS

The main key to developing a great chest is using plenty of variety in your pectoral workouts. Indeed, you can probably use the Weider Muscle Confusion Training Principle most effectively in your chest workouts. Simply do the same training program only once, moving on to a completely different type of workout the next time you are in the gym to train the chest.

Of course, you will always do some sort of Bench Press movement in your chest workouts, regardless of the type of incline, flat, or decline bench you use. But rather than always doing the exercise with a barbell, switch to using dumbbells or some type of pressing machine from time to time. And don't restrict yourself to using the same angles of incline and decline bench during every chest workout. An adjustable exercise bench will allow you to do your pressing movements and Flyes on a wide variety of bench angles and guarantee that you successfully use the Muscle Confusion Principle.

CHEST EXERCISES

It's essential that you correctly master each chest exercise described and illustrated in this section. If you don't do the movements correctly, you will receive less than optimum developmental value from them. And since it's very difficult to unlearn bad exercise habits, it's a better practice to learn the movements correctly from the very start of your bodybuilding involvement.

Bench Presses

Emphasis—This is one of the best of all upper body exercises. It places very direct stress on the entire pectoral complex as well as the anterior deltoids and triceps. Significant secondary stress is placed on the medial deltoids and the latissimus dorsi muscles.

Starting Position—Place a barbell on the support rack of a pressing bench and load the bar with an appropriate poundage for a set of Bench Presses. Lie back on the bench with your shoulder joints two or three inches toward the foot end of the bench from the support uprights. Place your feet flat on the floor on either side of the bench to balance your body in position as you do the movement. Take an overgrip on the bar with your hands set two or three inches wider on each side than your shoulders. Straighten your arms to lift the barbell off the rack and to a position supported at straight arms' length directly above your shoulder joints.

The Movement—Being sure that your upper arm bones travel directly out to the sides, slowly bend your arms and lower the barbell directly downward until it touches the lower part of your rib cage. Without bouncing at the bottom of the exercise, extend your arms and slowly push the weight back to the starting point. Repeat the exercise for the suggested number of reps.

Training Tips—The most common errors when performing Bench Presses are to arch your back and raise your hips from the bench to gain better pressing leverage and to bounce the bar off your chest. The former mistake removes stress from the sections of your pectorals that need it most, while the second error can cause an injury to your rib cage, your chest muscles, or your shoulder joints. You can get a lot more out of your Benches if you periodically vary the width of your grip on the bar inward until your hands are about 12 inches apart and outward to as wide a position as the length of the bar will permit.

Bench Press—start, top; finish, bottom.

Incline Press—start, left; finish, right.

Incline Presses

Emphasis—Doing Bench Presses on an incline bench stresses the same muscles as Benches on a flat bench, except that the upper pectorals receive proportionately more stress than the lower and outer chest muscles.

Starting Position—Place a barbell on the bench support rack and load it with an appropriate weight for a set of Inclines. Lie back on the bench, sitting on the adjustable seat to secure your position on the apparatus. Take an overgrip on the barbell with your hands set two or three inches wider than your shoulders on each side. Straighten your arms to lift the barbell off the rack to a supported position at straight arms' length directly above your shoulder joints (from the side, your arms will appear to be perpendicular to the floor).

The Movement—Being sure to keep your elbows well back, slowly bend your arms and lower the barbell downward to touch your upper chest at the base of your neck. Without bouncing the bar off your chest, push it steadily back to straight arms' length. Repeat the exercise for the required number of reps.

Training Tips—You can change the effect of Incline Presses on your upper chest muscles by varying the angle of the bench you use for the movement. Most frequently you will encounter a 45-degree incline bench, but often a lower angle (around 30 degrees) will give you better upper chest stimulation. Even using a very low incline (just a four-by-four-inch block of wood propped under the head end of the bench) will often give you excellent upper chest stimulation. And as with Bench Presses, you should occasionally vary the width of your grip on the barbell.

Decline Presses

Emphasis—Decline Presses stress the same muscles as Bench Presses performed on a flat bench, except that the bench angle change shifts primary pectoral stress to the lower and outer sections of the muscle group.

Starting Position—Few decline benches have racks attached, so you'll either need to have a training partner hand you the bar at straight arms' length or position the bench between the uprights of another weight support rack. Lie back on the bench, being sure to hook your toes beneath the restraint bar to secure your body in position on the bench throughout the movement. Either use the support rack or a training partner to take an overgrip on the bar with your hands set two or three inches wider than your shoulders on each side and bring the bar to straight arms' length directly above your shoulder joints.

The Movement—Being sure to keep your elbows well back, slowly bend your arms and lower the barbell downward to touch the lower edge of your chest lightly. Push the bar back to straight arms' length and repeat the movement for the suggested number of reps.

Training Tips—Normally, decline benches are set at about a 20- to 30-degree angle, but you can use benches set at lower or higher angles quite effectively. And you should periodically vary the width of your grip on the bar as you perform your Incline Presses.

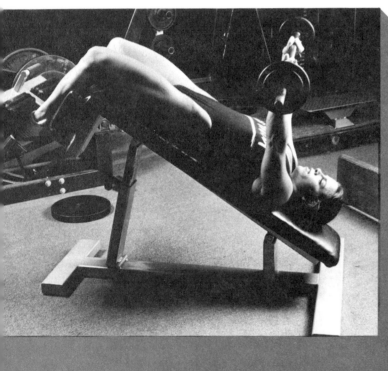

Decline Press—start, below; finish, right.

Dumbbell Bench Press (left) and Dumbbell Incline Press (right).

Dumbbell Bench Presses

Emphasis—Depending on the angle of the bench you use for this movement, you can place direct stress on almost any part of your pectoral muscle complex. Incline Bench Presses stress primarily the upper pectorals, Decline Presses stress the lower and outer pecs, and Dumbbell Bench Presses on a flat exercise bench stress the entire pectoral complex. Significant secondary stress is on the anterior deltoids and triceps, while ancillary stress is on the medial delts and latissimus dorsi muscles.

Starting Position—We'll describe performance of the Dumbbell Incline Press, because you can learn correct performance of the other two movements from this description. Grasp two moderately heavy dumbbells and sit down on the seat of an incline bench with the dumbbells resting on your knees. Simultaneously sit back on the incline bench and bring the dumbbells to your shoulders. Extend your arms straight up from your shoulders with your palms facing forward.

The Movement—Being sure to keep your elbows back, slowly bend your arms and lower the weights as far as you can toward and even past the level of your shoulders. Extend your arms and smoothly press the dumbbells back up to the starting point, touching them against each other directly above your chest. Repeat the exercise for the suggested number of reps.

Training Tips—You can also do Dumbbell Inclines with your palms facing each other rather than facing straight ahead. And you should periodically vary the angle of incline or decline of your angled benches.

Machine Bench Presses

Emphasis—You can also use a Smith machine, Universal Gym machine, or Nautilus machine (covered in the next exercise description) to stress all of the same muscles that you can emphasize with Bench Presses on a flat, incline, or decline bench. The main advantage of doing Benches on a machine is the safety factor; you won't be able to drop a loaded barbell across your body when you're using a pressing machine.

Starting Position—Place a flat, incline, or decline bench between the pressing handles of a Universal Gym machine or under the bar of a Smith machine. With the Universal Gym machine you'll be pressing the weight initially from the bottom position; and with a Smith machine, you can position the weight near the extended-arms point of the movement. Take an overgrip on the bar of handles with your hands set two or three inches wider than your shoulders on each side. If using a Universal Gym machine, extend your arms and press the weight upward to straight arms' length. And if using a Smith machine, push up on the bar a bit and rotate the pressing handle enough to release the bar from its safety stops.

The Movement—Slowly bend your arms and lower the bar down to touch your chest lightly. Push the bar evenly back to the starting point and repeat the movement for the suggested number of repetitions.

Training Tips—You should experiment with various grip widths and bench angles. And since you needn't control the bar as you lower it, you can also experiment with positioning your shoulders a little forward or backward of a point directly beneath the bar or pressing handles. Each new shoulder position automatically places a uniquely different stress on your pecs, delts, and triceps.

Incline Machine Bench Press—start, left; finish, right.

Nautilus Bench Presses

Emphasis—Bench Presses performed on a Nautilus double-shoulder machine stress primarily the lower and outer sections of your pectorals, plus your anterior deltoids and triceps. Secondary stress is placed on your medial deltoids and those upper back muscles that rotate your scapulae.

Starting Position—Adjust the height of the seat according to the specifications outlined in the description for Nautilus Flyes a bit later in this chapter. Sit down in the seat and fasten the seat belt across your lap. Lean back against the angled back support. Place your feet on the pedal directly in front of you and push down on the pedal to bring the machine's pressing handles upward far enough so you can grasp the ends of the handles with your palms toward each other. Extend your arms and press the handles out as far away from your body as possible.

The Movement—Slowly bend your arms and lower the pressing handles as far toward your body (and even past your torso) as possible. Without pausing, press them back away from yourself until your arms are straight. Repeat the movement for an appropriate number of repetitions.

Training Tips—This is a good movement for use of the Weider Retro-Gravity (negative reps) Training Principle. With the foot pedal, you can push out a weight much heavier than you can press out on your own, then resist the weight's downward momentum as you slowly lower it from the top point of the exercise back down to the starting position.

Nautilus Bench Press—start, left; finish, right.

Parallel Bar Dips

Emphasis—Parallel Bar Dips have an effect on your chest, shoulder, and arm muscles that is similar to that of Decline Presses. Dips stress the entire pectoral muscle complex, but particularly the lower and outer sections of the muscle group.

Starting Position—Grasp a pair of parallel bars so your palms are toward each other when you jump up to support yourself between the bars with your arms straight. Bend your legs at 90-degree angles and cross your ankles. Place your chin on your chest throughout the movement and lean your torso forward as you perform the exercise.

The Movement—Slowly bend your arms and lower your body between the bars as far as is comfortably possible. Push yourself slowly and steadily back up to the supported position and repeat the movement for the desired number of repetitions.

Training Tips—Many gyms have dipping bars that aren't actually parallel but rather angled inward on one end. These bars allow you to take a variety of grip widths for the exercise, the width of your grip determined by how close to the narrow end of the bars you happen to perform the movement. Regardless of the bars used, you will probably eventually grow strong enough to pump out more than 10–15 reps. At that point you will need to add resistance to the exercise, which is done most easily by hanging a light dumbbell around your waist with a loop of rope or nylon webbing. Simply secure the weight firmly to your body with the loop and hold it with leg pressure.

Parallel Bar Dips—start, left; finish, right.

Dumbbell Flyes—start, left; finish, below.

Dumbbell Flyes

Emphasis—Depending on the angle of bench you choose, you can stress your entire pectoral muscle complex (Flat Bench Flyes), your upper pecs (Incline Flyes), or your lower/outer pecs (Decline Flyes). Generally speaking, Dumbbell Flyes place the most stress on your pectorals out near your shoulder joints, rather than in closer to your sternum.

Starting Position—As with Dumbbell Bench Presses, we will describe the Incline Flyes. From this description you can easily learn Flat-Bench Flyes and Decline Flyes. Grasp two light dumbbells in your hands, sit back on an incline bench, and extend your arms directly up from your shoulders, your palms toward each other. Bend your arms slightly and keep them rounded like this throughout your set.

The Movement—Without rotating your wrists, slowly lower the dumbbells directly out to the sides and downward in semicircular arcs to as low a position as is comfortably possible. Be sure to keep your elbows back as you lower the weights. Use pectoral strength to return the dumbbells back along the same arcs to the starting point. Repeat the movement for the suggested number of repetitions.

Training Tips—In order to place more stress on your inner pecs, you must press the dumbbells together as hard as you can in the finish position directly above your chest. Be sure to experiment with a variety of bench angles when doing Incline Flyes and Decline Flyes.

Chris Glass demonstrates Incline Dumbbell Flyes.

Cable Flyes at finish.

Cable Flyes

Emphasis—Cable Flyes stress the same areas as Dumbbell Flyes but place greater stress on your inner pecs. You will feel this difference in your working muscles because the cables allow you to maintain resistance on your pecs in the finish position of the movement, something that is not possible with dumbbells.

Starting Position—Place a flat, incline, or decline bench between two floor pulleys. Attach loop handles to the floor pulleys. Grasp the handles and lie back on the bench. With your arms rounded and your palms toward each other, bring your hands together directly above your chest as in the start/finish position for Dumbbell Flyes.

The Movement—Feeling the resistance in your pectorals, slowly lower your hands directly out to the sides in semicircular arcs to as low a position as possible. Slowly return to the starting point and repeat the movement for an appropriate number of reps.

Training Tips—You'll soon learn that you can use heavier weights for Dumbbell Flyes and Cable Flyes if you bend your arms more. However, it's best to keep your arms bent only slightly and use lighter weights in the movement. And you should always keep in mind that the depth to which you lower the dumbbells in any variation of Flyes is not as important as how low your elbows travel.

Pec Deck Flyes

Emphasis—This excellent movement works the entire pectoral muscle complex quite intensely, even the hard-to-reach inner pecs. And it's an excellent exercise with which to practice the Weider Peak Contraction Training Principle for your pectorals.

Starting Position—Adjust the seat to a height that places your upper arms parallel with the floor when you are seated in the machine and correctly grasping the movement arms of the machine. Sit down on the seat and force your elbows and forearms behind the pads, your forearms running straight up the pads and your fingers lightly resting over the top edges of the pads. Allow the weight of the machine resistance to pull your elbows back behind your torso as far as possible, fully stretching your pectorals.

The Movement—Use pectoral strength to push with your elbows against the pads, moving the pads forward and toward each other until they touch in the middle directly in front of your chest. Hold this peak contracted position for a slow count of two, return evenly back to the starting point, and repeat the movement for the suggested number of repetitions.

Training Tips—Some pec deck machines allow you to do this exercise with one arm at a time. One-arm movements, as you probably know, place a much more intense stress on the working muscles than their two-armed counterparts. You can also vary the angle of stress on your pecs by adjusting the seat to a higher or lower level than you normally use.

Pec Deck Flyes—start, below; finish, right.

Nautilus Flyes

Emphasis—Nautilus Flyes are similar to Pec Deck Flyes, except that they stress primarily the lower, outer, and inner pecs versus the entire muscle as in Pec Deck Flyes.

Starting Position—Adjust the seat of the machine to a height that positions your upper arms parallel to the floor when you are sitting in the machine and have your arms correctly positioned on the movement arm pads. Sit down and secure the seat belt over your lap. Force your elbows behind the movement pads, lightly resting your fingers over one of the two sets of handles. Allow the pads to pull your elbows to the rear as far as is comfortably possible.

The Movement—Use pectoral strength to push with your elbows against the pads to move them forward and toward each other until they touch together directly in front of your chest. Hold this peak contracted position for a moment, return slowly to the starting point, and repeat the exercise for an appropriate number of reps.

Training Tips—Near the pivot points of the lever arms on each side you will find handles that you can conveniently grasp with your free hand whenever you do this exercise with one arm at a time. You can also position the machine seat a little higher or lower than normal when you do Nautilus Flyes.

Nautilus Flyes—start, below left; finish, below right.

Cable Crossovers—start, below; finish, right.

Cable Crossovers

Emphasis—Competitive bodybuilders use Cable Crossovers most frequently during a peaking cycle to add to the number of striations across their pectorals. Crossovers place maximum stress on the lower, outer, and inner pecs. Secondary stress is placed on the anterior deltoids.

Starting Point—Attach loop handles to two high pulleys, grasp the handles with your palms toward the floor, stand directly between the pulleys with your feet set about shoulder width apart, and extend your arms upward from your shoulders at 45-degree angles with the floor. You will probably find that you get more out of this movement if your torso is inclined slightly forward from your waist.

The Movement—Use pectoral strength to move your hands downward and slightly forward in semicircular arcs until they touch each other about six to eight inches in front of your hips. Hold this peak contracted position of the movement for a slow count of two, return smoothly to the starting point, and repeat the exercise for the required number of reps.

Training Tips—You can vary the area of your pecs that this movement hits by leaning forward more acutely at the waist. If you actually lean forward until your torso is parallel to the floor, you will be doing a movement very similar to Flat-Bench Cable Flyes. Cable Crossovers can also be performed with one arm at a time, your free hand resting on your hip.

Stiff-Arm Pullovers

Emphasis—All types of Pullovers place very direct stress on the serratus, pectoral, and latissimus dorsi muscles.

Starting Position—Take a shoulder-width overgrip on a light barbell. Lie on your back on a flat exercise bench, your head hanging off the end of the bench and your feet planted firmly on the floor. Extend your arms straight up from your shoulders. Straighten your arms and keep them straight throughout the movement.

The Movement—Slowly lower the barbell backward and downward in a semicircular arc to as low a position as is comfortably possible behind your head. You should inhale as you lower the bar. Slowly return the barbell back along the same arc to the starting point, exhaling en route. Repeat the exercise for the suggested number of reps.

Training Tips—You can also do this movement with two light dumbbells held in your hands or a single light dumbbell held in both hands. Stiff-Arm Pullovers can also be performed profitably on lower incline or decline benches.

Stiff-Arm Pullovers—start, left; finish, below.

Cross-Bench Pullovers—start, left; finish, below.

Cross-Bench Pullovers

Emphasis—Cross-Bench Pullovers stress the same muscle groups as Stiff-Arm Pullovers. If you happen to be working your chest and back in the same training session, you will find that Cross-Bench Pullovers are the best transitional movement between the two body parts.

Starting Position—Place a moderately heavy dumbbell on end on top of a flat exercise bench (it should be placed toward one end of the bench). Lie across the bench with only your shoulders and upper body in contact with the bench and place your feet shoulder width apart on the floor to balance your body in position. Bend your legs appropriately. Place your palms flat against the inner side of the upper set of plates, encircling the bar with your thumbs to keep the weight from slipping out of your hands. Pull the dumbbell over to a supported position at straight arms' length directly above your chest.

The Movement—Simultaneously bend your arms slightly and lower the dumbbell in a semicircular arc from the starting point to the rear and downward to as low a position as possible. Follow the same breathing pattern as for Stiff-Arm Pullovers. Return the dumbbell to the starting point, simultaneously straightening your arms. Repeat.

Training Tips—You can get a better stretch in your pectoral, serratus, and latissimus dorsi muscles if you lower your hips four to six inches as you reach the bottom position of the movement. You can also do Bent-Arm Pullovers, a movement very similar to a barbell, while lying lengthwise along the bench.

SUGGESTED CHEST ROUTINES

While this book is intended primarily for intermediate and advanced bodybuilders and weight trainers, there may be a few beginners reading this chapter. We define a beginner as any woman with less than six to eight weeks of training behind her. Following is a beginning-level chest program that can be used on three nonconsecutive days per week:

Exercise	Sets	Reps
Incline Presses	3	8–12
Flat-Bench Flyes	2	8–12

After you have completed six to eight weeks on the foregoing program, you can move up to the following low-intermediate routine, which can be performed on three nonconsecutive days per week:

Exercise	Sets	Reps
Incline Dumbbell Presses	3	8–12
Decline Machine Presses	3	8–12
Flat-Bench Cable Flyes	2	8–12

Another six to eight weeks of training will bring you to the full intermediate level of training. At that point you can use the following chest routine on three nonconsecutive days per week:

Exercise	Sets	Reps
Incline Machine Presses	4	8–12
Parallel Bar Dips	3	8–12
Pec Deck Flyes	3	8–12
Cross-Bench Pullovers	2–3	8–12

Advanced bodybuilders during off-season workouts normally follow a four-day split routine (see Chapter 10) in which they train half of their bodies on Mondays and Thursdays and the other half on Tuesdays and Fridays. Therefore, they train only twice per week, which allows them to place much greater stress on the body part during each session. Following is a sample off-season training program that can be used two days per week:

Exercise	Sets	Reps
Incline Barbell Presses	4	8–12
Decline Dumbbell Presses	4	8–12
Low-Incline Dumbbell Flyes	3	8–12
Pec Deck Flyes	3	8–12
Stiff-Arm Pullovers (low incline)	2–3	8–12

CHEST ROUTINES OF THE CHAMPIONS

It's important to understand that the routines presented in this section are of extremely high intensity. If you have less than a year of solid, all-out training behind you, you won't make gains using any of these programs. And it's likely that you will soon overtrain using one of these routines, which can even lead to a regression in your physical development. However, by scaling these routines down to your own ability levels, you can make good progress with them. Simply do the same exercises as your favorite champion but perform fewer sets of each movement.

Carla Dunlap
(Miss Olympia)

Exercise	Sets	Reps
Incline Dumbbell Presses	4	8–10
Decline Dumbbell Presses	4	8–10
Decline Pullovers	4	8–10
Pec Deck Flyes	4	8–10

Laura Combes
(Ms. America)

Exercise	Sets	Reps
Incline Dumbbell Presses	4–6	10–12
Parallel Bar Dips (weighted)	4–5	10–12
Pec Deck Flyes	4–5	10–12
Decline Barbell Presses	4–5	10–12
Incline Dumbbell Flyes	4–5	10–12
Cross-Bench Pullovers	3–4	10–12
Cable Crossovers	3–4	12–15

Patsy Chapman
(Best-in-the-World Champ)

Exercise	Sets	Reps
Bench Presses	5	10
Flat-Bench Flyes	5	10
Incline Barbell Presses	5	10

Lisa Elliott-Kolakowski
(Ms. Eastern America)

Exercise	Sets	Reps
Incline Dumbell Presses	4–5	6–8
Incline Dumbell Flyes	4–5	6–8
Machine Bench Presses	4–5	6–8
Pec Deck Flyes	4–5	6–8
Decline Cable Flyes	4–5	8–10

Shelley Gruwell
(World Grand Prix Champion)

Exercise	Sets	Reps
Flat-Bench Dumbbell Flyes	3	8–10
Dumbbell Bench Presses (flat bench)	3	8–10
Machine Bench Presses (flat bench)	3	8–10
Incline Barbell Press	2–3	8–10
Cable Crossovers	2–3	10–15

Corrine Machado-Ching
(Ms. Western America)

Exercise	Sets	Reps
Incline Dumbbell Presses	4	6–10
Flat-Bench Dumbell Flyes	3	8–10
Parallel Bar Dips	3	8–10
Cross-Bench Pullovers	3	8–10

Candy Csencsits
(Ms. Eastern America)

Exercise	Sets	Reps
Incline Barbell Presses	3–4	8–12
Pec Deck Flyes	3–4	8–12
Decline Dumbbell Flyes	3–4	8–12
Cable Crossovers	3–4	10–15

Inger Zetterqvist
(World Champion)

Exercise	Sets	Reps
Barbell Bench Presses	3–4	10–12
Parallel Bar Dips	2–3	10–12
Pec Deck Flyes	2–3	10–12
Cable Crossovers	2–3	10–12
Cross-Bench Pullovers	2–3	10–12

Dr. Lynne Pirie
(Superbowl of Bodybuilding Champ)

Exercise	Sets	Reps
Incline Dumbbell Presses	3–4	6–10
Nautilus Flyes	2–3	8–10
Parallel Bar Dips	2–3	8–10
Flat-Bench Dumbbell Flyes	2–3	8–10

Pirjo Haapalo, from Finland, placed second at the 1983 World Championships.

Lisa Elliott-Kolakowski, Gold's Classic Champion.

7
DYNAMIC DELTS

Complete shoulder development is absolutely essential for a competitive bodybuilder because it's impossible to disguise subpar deltoids in a posing routine. Whether your physique is viewed from the front, back, or side, the deltoids are always clearly visible. The delts can also be seen whether your arms are held down at your sides, directly out at the sides, or straight overhead.

Optimum shoulder development is also important onstage at a competition because it lends width to your shoulder structure. While a few of the more androgynous women have naturally broad shoulders and narrow hips, most competitive women bodybuilders have wide hips and comparatively narrow shoulder structures. And without developing your deltoids to the limit, this negative differential between your hips and shoulders will ruin the symmetry of your body.

For athletes—regardless of the sport— powerful shoulder development greatly enhances athletic performance. A cursory glance at the range of motion permitted by your shoulder joint will convince you that it's impossible to move either of your arms without strongly involving your deltoid muscles. And for optimum sports performance, you should be able to use deltoid strength to move your arms with great power.

Health- and fitness-minded women should also pay attention to toning and strengthening the muscles of their shoulder girdles. The shoulder muscles—and particularly the trapezius group of your upper back—are responsible for helping you maintain perfect upper body posture. And strong deltoids will help you excel at recreational athletic activities, such as tennis or racquetball.

SHOULDER ANATOMY AND KINESIOLOGY

The primary muscle mass of your shoulders is the deltoid, which forms a rounded cap over the point of your shoulder when it is fully developed. Originating from the clavicular bone, the deltoid forms three heads (or lobes) that insert via a common tendon into your humerus (or upper arm bone). These deltoid heads contract to help move your arm in a wide variety of directions, as well as to help rotate your arm in the shoulder socket.

The anterior (front) head of your deltoid contracts to move your upper arm bone forward as well as out to the side when your palm is facing either forward or upward. The medial (side) head of your deltoid contracts to move your upper arm out to the side when your palm is down. And your posterior (rear) deltoid head contracts to move your humerus to the rear.

Around the shoulder joint itself is a small bundle of muscles called the *rotator cuff*. These smaller muscles help rotate the arm in its shoulder socket, as well as to initiate movement of your humerus away from the side of your torso. Since these muscles are small and relatively weak, they can easily be injured if you try to use a very heavy weight in any of several deltoid exercises prior to warming up thoroughly.

Most bodybuilders consider the trapezius muscle to be an upper back muscle. Since it does exert a force that moves the shoulder girdle, however, some bodybuilders consider the trapezius muscle group to be part of the shoulders. (Refer back to Chapter 5 for information on the anatomy, kinesiology, and development of the trapezius.)

SHOULDER TRAINING SECRETS

The shoulder joint is a shallow ball-and-socket joint that is structurally very weak. This joint weakness and the lack of strength in your rotator cuff muscle complex make your shoulders relatively susceptible to injury. Indeed, many bodybuilders have been forced out of the sport after suffering very serious shoulder injuries.

Due to its weak structure, you should always thoroughly warm up your shoulder joints—as well as the surrounding mus-

cles—prior to using even moderately heavy weights in your shoulder workouts. This warm-up should include stretching exercises, free-hand calisthenic movements, and plenty of high-rep light training with weights prior to working up to maximum poundages.

Since the deltoids are capable of exerting such a variety of forces on your upper arm bone, you will be able to develop them fully only if you consistently include three types of exercises in your shoulder routines—pushing movements (Barbell/Dumbbell/Machine Presses), leverage exercises (Front/Side/Bent Laterals) and pulling movements (Upright Rows). The best women bodybuilders make liberal use of all three types of movements in their shoulder training programs.

SHOULDER EXERCISES

It's essential that you correctly master each deltoid exercise listed in this section. If you don't do the movements correctly, you will receive very little developmental value from them. And since it's very difficult to unlearn bad exercise habits, it's best to learn the exercises correctly from the very start.

Standing Barbell Presses

Emphasis—Barbell Presses stress primarily the anterior deltoid heads and the triceps. Significant secondary stress is placed on the medial and posterior delts as well as on the upper chest and upper back muscles.

Starting Position—Place a barbell on the floor at your feet, bend over, and take an overgrip on the barbell with your hands set two or three inches wider than your shoulders on each side of the bar. Dip your hips below the level of your shoulders and pull the barbell up to rest across your shoulders. Rotate your elbows beneath the bar and keep them directly beneath the bar thoughout the movement. Stand erect with your feet set about shoulder width apart and refrain from bending back at the waist as you perform the exercise.

Standing Barbell Press—start, above; finish, right.

The Movement—Slowly straighten your arms and push the barbell directly upward from your shoulders until it is at straight arms' length above your shoulder joints. Slowly lower the bar back to your shoulders and immediately initiate another repetition. Continue the set until you have completed the required number of repetitions.

Training Tips—To isolate your legs from the movement you can perform Seated Barbell Presses while seated on a flat exercise bench, particularly one that has an upright padded surface that supports your torso in a vertical position as you do the exercise. Regardless of whether you do Presses standing or seated, you can vary the width of your grip on the bar to stimulate your deltoids from different angles.

Press behind Neck—start, left; midpoint (on Smith machine), right.

Presses behind Neck

Emphasis—Pressing the bar up from behind your neck rather than from in front of it places very direct stress on your anterior deltoids and triceps. Significant secondary stress is placed on your posterior and medial deltoid heads plus your upper chest and upper back muscles.

Starting Position—Presses behind Neck are usually performed seated on an exercise bench. Take an overgrip on a barbell with your hands set one or two inches wider on each side than for Standing Barbell Presses. Pull the barbell up to your shoulders and push it up over your head to a position resting across your trapezius muscles behind your neck. Sit down on the exercise

bench and rotate your elbows beneath the bar.

The Movement—Without moving any part of your body but your arms, slowly push the barbell directly upward until it is at straight arms' length above your shoulder joints. Slowly lower the barbell back to the starting point and repeat the movement for the suggested number of repetitions.

Training Tips—You can also do this exercise in a standing position, and you can vary the width of your grip on the bar. With all types of Barbell Presses you can lift the barbell off a squat rack to the correct position across your shoulders rather than pulling it from the floor up to your shoulders.

Dumbbell Presses

Emphasis—As with various forms of Barbell Presses, Dumbbell Presses place primary stress on the anterior deltoids and triceps. Secondary emphasis is put on the medial and posterior deltoids as well as the upper chest and upper back muscles.

Starting Position—Grasp two moderately heavy dumbbells and pull them to your shoulders, rotating your hands so your palms are facing forward during the exercise. Be sure that your feet are set about shoulder width apart and stand erect throughout the movement.

The Movement—Keeping your elbows directly under the weights, slowly push the dumbbells directly upward until they are at straight arms' length and touching each other directly above your head. Lower the weights under control back to the starting point and repeat the movement.

Training Tips—Dumbbell Presses can also be performed with your palms facing inward (toward each other) rather than facing forward. You can perform the movement in an alternating fashion, one dumbbell going upward as the other descends. And you can do all of these variations of Dumbbell Presses while seated on a flat exercise bench.

Dumbbell Press—start, left; finish, right.

Machine Presses

Emphasis—The various types of Machine Presses place direct stress on your anterior delts and triceps. Secondary emphasis is placed on your medial and posterior delts plus the upper chest and upper back muscles.

Starting Position (Universal Gym)—Place a stool directly beneath the pressing handles of the machine. Sit on the stool, facing the weight stack, and grasp the middle of each handle. Rotate your elbows downward until they are directly beneath your hands as you perform the exercise.

Starting Position (Nautilus)—Adjust the height of the seat on a Nautilus double-shoulder machine so your shoulder joints are level with the pressing handles when you sit in the seat. Sit down, fasten the seat belt over your lap, and cross your ankles beneath the seat. With your palms facing each other, grasp the pressing handles and rotate your elbows downward until they are directly beneath your hands.

The Movement—With all three types of apparatus, slowly straighten your arms to push the handles or bar to straight arms' length. Slowly return to the starting position and repeat the movement for an appropriate number of reps.

Training Tips—On a Universal machine you can also perform the exercise facing away from the machine, as well as with one arm at a time, either facing toward or away from the machine. On a Nautilus machine the exercise can be performed with one arm at a time. And on a Smith machine you can also do Machine Presses behind Neck.

Machine Press (Universal Gym)—start, left; finish, above.

Nautilus Press—start, above; finish, below.

Front Raises—start, left; finish, below.

Front Raises

Emphasis—Front lateral raises place primary stress on the anterior heads of the deltoids and secondary emphasis on the medial delts.

Starting Position—Take a shoulder-width overgrip on a light barbell. Set your feet about shoulder width apart and stand erect with your arms straight down at your sides and the barbell resting across your upper thighs. Keep your arms straight throughout the movement.

The Movement—Use deltoid strength to raise the barbell slowly in a semicircular arc from the starting point upward until it is slightly above shoulder level. Lower the weight back to the starting point and repeat the movement.

Training Tips—This exercise is also frequently done holding two light dumbbells. In this movement your palms should be toward the floor as you do the exercise, and you should do the movement in an alternating fashion, one dumbbell being raised up to shoulder level while the other is being lowered back to the starting point.

Dumbbell Side Laterals—start, left; finish, below.

Dumbbell Side Laterals

Emphasis—All variations of Side Lateral Raises isolate stress on the medial deltoid heads. Minor secondary stress is put on the anterior delts (this stress will be minor only if the movement is performed correctly).

Starting Position—Grasp two light dumbbells, place your feet about shoulder width apart, and stand erect. With your palms facing each other, press the dumbbells together three or four inches in front of your hips. Bend your arms slightly and keep them rounded like this as you do the movement. You should also incline your torso slightly forward throughout your set.

The Movement—Using deltoid strength, slowly raise the dumbbells out to the sides and upward in semicircular arcs until they are slightly above shoulder level. It's essential at the top point of the movement that your index fingers are slightly below the level of your little fingers. Slowly lower the dumbbells back along the same arcs to the starting point and repeat the movement for the desired number of repetitions.

Training Tips—A very similar movement is frequently performed while lying facedown on a high incline bench. In a standing position you can do Dumbbell Side Laterals with one arm at a time, grasping a sturdy upright with your free hand to brace your body in position as you perform the exercise.

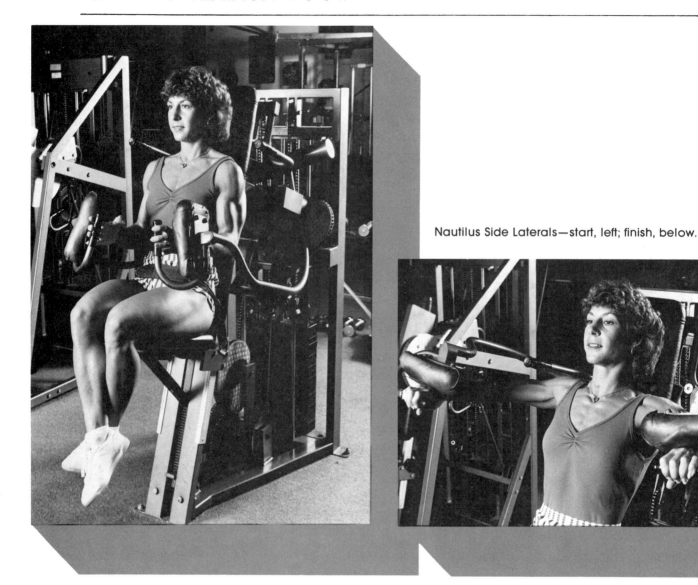

Nautilus Side Laterals—start, left; finish, below.

Nautilus Side Laterals

Emphasis—Side Laterals performed on a Nautilus double-shoulder machine isolate stress on the medial deltoid heads. Minor secondary stress is placed on the anterior deltoids.

Starting Position—Adjust the height of the seat so your shoulder joints are at the same level as the pivot points of the machine when you are sitting in the apparatus. Sit on the seat, fasten the seat belt over your lap, and cross your ankles beneath yourself. With your palms facing inward (toward each other), place the backs of your wrists against the pads attached to the movement arms of the machine. Grasp the handles attached to the pads.

The Movement—Use medial deltoid strength to slowly move the pads out to the sides and upward until they are slightly above shoulder level. Hold this top position for a moment, lower back to the starting point, and repeat the movement.

Training Tips—Keep in mind that the object of this exercise is to move your elbows upward rather than your hands, which merely trail behind your elbow movement. You can also do this exercise in a standing position, facing toward the machine rather than away from it.

Cable Side Laterals—start, left; finish, below.

Cable Side Laterals

Emphasis—Cable Side Laterals place direct stress on the medial heads of your deltoids. Minor secondary stress is on your anterior deltoids.

Starting Position—Attach a loop handle to the cable running through a floor pulley and grasp the handle in your left hand. Stand with your right foot one or two feet from the pulley, your right side directly toward the pulley and the cable running directly across the front of your body. Bend your left arm slightly and keep it rounded like this throughout the movement. Place your right hand on your hip. Move your left hand toward the pulley until it is at least six to eight inches past the midline of your body.

The Movement—Keeping your hand slightly in front of your body, move the handle in a semicircular arc from the starting point out to the left side and upward until your hand is slightly above the level of your shoulder. Return the pulley handle back along the same arc to the starting point and repeat the movement for the suggested number of repetitions.

Training Tips—You can also do Cable Side Laterals with the cable running across the back of your body, a movement that puts a much different stress on your deltoids. It's also possible to do this exercise with both hands simultaneously by using two floor pulleys and crossing the cables in front of your body (i.e., the cable on the right side of your body runs up to your left hand and the cable on the left side of your body runs up to your right hand).

Dumbbell Bent Laterals—start, above; finish, below.

Dumbbell Bent Laterals

Emphasis—All variations of Bent Laterals place direct stress on the posterior deltoids and significant secondary stress on the upper back muscles.

Starting Position—Grasp two light dumbbells in your hands and set your feet about shoulder width apart. Bend over at the waist until your torso is parallel to the floor and unlock your legs slightly to keep unnecessary stress off your lower back. Your arms should be hanging straight down from your shoulders, your palms facing inward (toward each other). Bend your arms slightly and keep them rounded like this throughout your set. Lightly press the dumbbells together directly beneath your chest.

The Movement—Without moving any part of your body but your arms, slowly raise the dumbbells in semicircular arcs out to the sides and upward until they are slightly above the level of your shoulders. It's important that you raise the dumbbells directly out from your shoulders rather than somewhat to the rear, which is a common beginner's mistake. Slowly lower the weights back along the same arcs to the starting point and repeat the movement for the required number of reps.

Training Tips—This movement is often performed while seated at the end of a flat exercise bench, bending forward until your torso is resting along the tops of your thighs. In a standing position you can do Bent Laterals one arm at a time while grasping a sturdy upright to steady your torso in position. Just be sure that you do an equal number of sets and reps for each side of your body.

Seated Dumbbell Bent Laterals at finish.

Cable Bent Laterals

Emphasis—As with Dumbbell Bent Laterals, this exercise places direct stress on the posterior deltoids and significant secondary stress on the upper back muscles.

Starting Position—Attach loop handles to two floor pulleys and stand directly between the pulleys. Reach to your right with your left hand and grasp the handle attached to the pulley on that side. Then reach to your left with your right hand and grasp the handle attached to the pulley on that side. This should put you in a position with your arms crossed. Bend over until your torso is parallel to the floor and allow the weights attached to the cables to pull your arms across each other directly beneath your torso.

The Movement—Slowly move your hands in semicircular arcs out to the sides and upward until they are slightly above the level of your shoulders. Hold this top position for a moment, return to the starting point, and repeat the movement for the appropriate number of repetitions.

Training Tips—You can also do this exercise with one arm at a time by holding the cable handle in the hand farthest from the pulley and allowing the weight to pull your hand as far as possible across your chest and toward the pulley at the starting point of the movement. You'll find it most convenient to rest your free hand on your knee to help brace your torso in a position parallel to the floor.

Cable Bent Laterals—start, left; finish, below.

Upright Rows—start, left; finish, below.

Upright Rows

Emphasis—This is an excellent all-around exercise for your shoulder girdle muscles. Upright Rows place direct stress on your medial delts, posterior delts, and trapezius. Meaningful secondary stress is placed on your anterior deltoids, biceps, brachialis, and the gripping muscles of your forearms.

Starting Position—Take a narrow overgrip in the middle of a barbell handle (there should be about six inches of space showing between your index fingers). Place your feet about shoulder width apart and stand erect with your arms straight down at your sides and your hands with the barbell in them resting across your upper thighs.

The Movement—Keeping the weight two or three inches in front of your body, slowly pull it directly upward until your hands touch the underside of your chin. As you pull the weight upward, it's essential that your elbows always be kept above the level of your hands. At the top of the movement, squeeze your shoulder blades together, hold the contracted position for a moment, and return the weight to the starting point. Repeat.

Training Tips—A very similar movement can be performed by attaching a short bar handle to a floor pulley. Or you can perform a somewhat similar exercise holding two dumbbells in your hands.

SUGGESTED SHOULDER ROUTINES

While this book is intended primarily for intermediate and advanced weight trainers and bodybuilders, there may be a few beginners reading this chapter. We define a beginner as any woman with less than six to eight weeks of training experience behind her. Following is a beginning-level deltoid program that can be used on three nonconsecutive days per week:

Exercise	Sets	Reps
Standing Barbell Presses	3	6–10
Barbell Upright Rows	2	8–12

After you have completed six to eight weeks on the foregoing program, you can move up to the following low-intermediate routine, which you can perform on three nonconsecutive days per week:

Exercise	Sets	Reps
Presses behind Neck	3	6–10
Dumbbell Side Laterals	2	8–12
Dumbbell Bent Laterals	2	8–12

Another six to eight weeks of training will bring you to the full intermediate level of training. At that point you can use the following deltoid routine on three nonconsecutive days per week:

Exercise	Sets	Reps
Smith Machine Front Presses	3	6–10
Dumbbell Side Laterals	2–3	8–12
Cable Bent Laterals	3	8–12
Barbell Upright Rows	2–3	8–12

During off-season workouts advanced bodybuilders normally follow a four-day split routine (see Chapter 10) in which they train half of their bodies on Mondays and Thursdays and the other half on Tuesdays and Fridays. Therefore, they train deltoids only twice per week, which allows them to place much greater stress on that body part. Following is a sample off-season training program that can be used two days per week:

Exercise	Sets	Reps
Seated Dumbbell Presses	4	6–10
Front Raises	3	8–12
Cable Side Laterals	3	8–12
Seated Dumbbell Bent Laterals	3–4	8–12
Cable Upright Rows	3	8–12

Every competitive bodybuilder trains differently prior to a major championship because she has learned precisely what works best for her unique body. In the following section you will find several examples of precontest delt routines used by some of the greatest Weider-trained IFBB superstars.

DELTOID ROUTINES OF THE CHAMPIONS

It's important to understand that the routines presented in this section are of extremely high intensity. If you have less than a year of solid, all-out training behind you, you won't make gains using any of these programs. And it's likely that you will soon overtrain using one of these routines, which can even lead to a regression in your physical development. However, by scaling these routines down to your own ability levels, you can make good progress with them. Simply do the same exercises as your favorite champion, but perform fewer sets of each movement.

Lori Bowen
(American Champion)

Exercise	Sets	Reps
Machine Presses	3–4	10–15
Machine Side Laterals	3–4	10–15
Dumbbell Bent Laterals	3–4	10–15
Cable Upright Rows	3–4	10–15

Laura Combes
(American Champion)

Exercise	Sets	Reps
Standing Barbell Presses (warm-up)	2–3	10–15
Dumbbell Presses	4–5	8–10
Machine Presses	3–4	8–10
Prone Incline Side Laterals	3–4	8–10
Dumbbell Side Laterals	3–4	8–10
Dumbbell Bent Laterals	4–5	8–10
Upright Rows	2–3	8–10

Inger Zetterqvist
(World Champion)

Exercise	Sets	Reps
Universal Machine Presses	3	10–12
Alternate Dumbbell Presses	2–3	10–12
Dumbbell Side Laterals	2	10–12
One-Arm Cable Side Laterals	2	10–12
Seated Dumbbell Bent Laterals	2	10–12
One-Arm Cable Bent Laterals	2	10–12

Rachel McLish
(Miss Olympia)

Exercise	Sets	Reps
Standing Barbell Presses (warm-up)	2–3	20–30
Nautilus Side Laterals	2–3	10–15
supersetted with . . .		
Nautilus Presses	2–3	10–15
Dumbbell Bent Laterals	3	10–15
Barbell Upright Rows	1–2	10–15

Sue Ann McKean
(Superbowl Champion)

Exercise	Sets	Reps
Seated Presses behind Neck	4–5	10–6
Dumbbell Alternate Front Raises	3–4	8–12
Dumbbell Side Laterals	3–4	8–12
One-Arm Cable Side Laterals	3–4	8–12
Standing Dumbbell Bent Laterals	3–4	8–12
Seated Dumbbell Bent Laterals	3–4	8–12
Smith Machine Front Presses	2–3	6–10

Candy Csencsits
(Miss Olympia Runner-Up)

Exercise	Sets	Reps
Machine Presses	3–4	10–12
Upright Rows	3–4	10–12
Cable Side Laterals	3–4	10–12
Dumbbell Bent Laterals	3–4	10–12
Dumbbell Presses	3–4	10–12

Dinah Anderson, the 1983 Middleweight American Champion.

Gold's Classic Champion, Pillow.

8
ARMED TO WIN

While it's relatively easy for most serious women bodybuilders to develop an outstanding pair of legs, arm development is comparatively difficult for most women to achieve. Few and far between are biceps developments as good as that of Rachel McLish (Miss Olympia) and Carla Dunlap (Miss Olympia), triceps like Kay Baxter's (Gold's Classic Champion) and Lynn Conkwright's (Pro World Champion), forearm development like that of Bev Francis (world record–holding powerlifter turned successful competitive bodybuilder) and Deborah Diana (USA Champion), or the great overall arm development of Laura Combes (the first American Women's Bodybuilding Champion) and Julie McNew (USA Couples Champ). It's difficult to build great arms, but it obviously can be done!

Competitive bodybuilders should aim for a pleasing combination of proportionate muscle mass, attractive shape, and sharp muscularity. And this high quality of arm development is essential because it's difficult to camouflage weak arms onstage, particularly in the round of mandatory poses. In that round you are forced to do double-biceps shots from both the front and back, and weak arm development will be painfully obvious in these two poses.

Serious athletes in other sports also require strong arm development because there are very few sports in which the arms do not come into play. And when you do use your arms in your sport you should do so with speed and power built through hard weight training. Even if your arms don't play a major role in your sport, you should still take care to strengthen them fully. Our theory of sports conditioning is that a chain is only as strong as its weakest link, so an athlete should take care to strengthen every part of her body.

Finally, health- and fitness-minded women

should include arm exercises in their weight routines in order to prevent their upper arms from turning to mush, which so often happens as you pass out of your 20s and into your 30s. Proper exercise habits and maintenance of a sensible diet can prevent this unsightly condition for a lifetime.

ARM ANATOMY AND KINESIOLOGY

We usually think of arm anatomy in terms of three main areas— the biceps, triceps, and forearms. The biceps is actually a somewhat smaller muscle group than the triceps. It is situated on the front of your upper arm, originating from attachments at your shoulder joint, separating into two distinct bellies of muscle (hence the *bi* in biceps), and then inserting via a large tendon to the forearm bone. The biceps contracts to flex the arm completely from a straight position and to supinate the hand (turn your palm from a position facing the floor to one facing the ceiling when you are standing erect and your arm is bent at a right angle).

Beneath the biceps lies the brachialis, a flat muscle group that runs only about halfway up the upper arm bone from the elbow joint. The brachialis also assists in flexing your arm, particularly when your hand is in a pronated position, as when performing Reverse Curls with a barbell. From the rear, you can see the brachialis as a well-defined band of muscle between the triceps and biceps when a very muscular woman bodybuilder flexes her arm.

The triceps is a three-headed muscle that lies on the back of your upper arm. Also originating from attachments near your shoulder joints, it attaches via a large, flat tendon over your elbow to your forearm bone. Your triceps contracts primarily to straighten your arm from a flexed position. Secondarily, it can contract to move your entire straight arm toward the rear.

There are three primary muscle groups in your forearms, though there are many separate muscles in each of these groups. This is certainly understandable, for the human hand is one of the most precisely engineered grasping devices on earth. It can grasp with the savagery of a person defending her life or with an adroit fineness that allows for brain surgery.

The forearm flexors lie along the inner sides of your forearms. They contract both to close your hands and to flex your wrists. The forearm extensors run along the outer sides of your forearms. They contract to open your hands and to extend your wrists. And the powerful supinators lie on the upper and outer sections of your forearms. These muscles contract to help supinate your hand and to bend your arm when your hand is in a pronated position.

ARM TRAINING SECRETS

The main secret to arm training is to avoid overtraining these small muscle groups. In most basic exercises for your torso muscle groups your biceps and triceps also come into play. For example, your biceps strongly contract in Barbell Row, Dumbbell Row, and Pulley Row movements. And your triceps strongly contract in Overhead Presses, Incline Presses, Bench Presses, and Parallel Bar Dips. So when you add 12–15 additional sets of direct biceps and direct triceps training to your program it's very easy to see why you will soon overtrain your upper arms. As you know, overtraining will prevent your muscles from growing and in some extreme cases will even result in a regression in development.

With upper arm training a good rule to follow is actually to undertrain your biceps and triceps. Beginning bodybuilders (those with less than about six months of training behind them) need do only four to six total sets for each muscle. With between 6 and 12 months of steady training you can profit from doing six to eight total sets for each muscle group. And at the advanced level you will never need to do more than 8–10 total sets for biceps or triceps.

Incidentally, you can normally do just one or two more total sets for your triceps than for your biceps because your triceps have about 30 percent more mass than your biceps. Generally speaking, we believe in doing

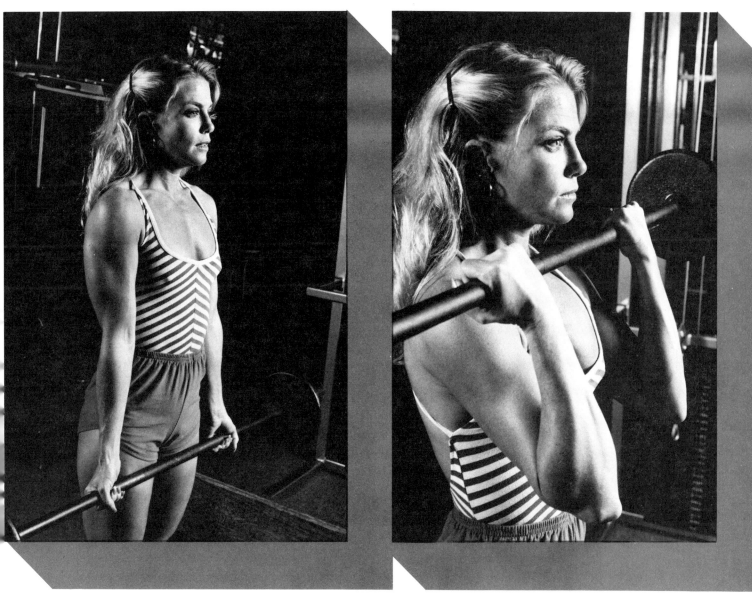

Barbell Curl—start, left; finish, right.

more total sets for larger muscle groups than for smaller body parts. Therefore, you should have no trepidations about doing a bit more triceps work.

ARM EXERCISES

Twenty arm exercises are fully described and clearly illustrated in this chapter. With variations on exercises, this will give you more than 40 arm movements to include in your workouts. Be cautious, however, that you learn to perform each movement correctly from the very first time you touch a weight. Poor exercise form provides less stimulation than scrupulously strict form, and poor workout habits are very difficult to correct three or four years down the road.

Barbell Curls

Emphasis—This is the most basic of all biceps movements. It powerfully stresses the biceps muscles and places significant secondary stress on the flexor muscles of your forearms.

Starting Position—Take an undergrip on a barbell with your hands set slightly wider than your shoulders on each side. Place your feet a comfortable distance apart and stand erect with your arms running straight down at your sides and the barbell resting across your upper thighs. Keep your upper arms pressed against the sides of your rib cage throughout your set.

The Movement—Moving only your forearms, use biceps strength to curl the barbell in a semicircular arc from your thighs to a position directly beneath your chin. You can start the movement with your wrists held straight and finish it with them flexed. Slowly lower the weight back to the starting point and repeat the movement for the required number of repetitions. Be very careful not to allow your torso to move forward and backward as you do your set of Barbell Curls.

Training Tips—If you have difficulty with torso swing as you perform Barbell Curls, you can eliminate the problem by doing the exercise with your back resting against either the gym wall or a sturdy upright post. On all of your Barbell Curls you can also vary the width of your grip on the bar, from one as wide as the length of the bar permits to one as narrow as with your hands touching in the middle of the bar. Each change of grip width attacks your biceps from a slightly different angle.

Dumbbell Curls

Emphasis—As with Barbell Curls, Dumbbell Curls place strong stress on your biceps and secondary stress on your forearm flexors. However, due to the supination factor with dumbbells, you'll probably achieve a somewhat better effect with Dumbbell Curls than with Barbell Curls.

Starting Position—Grasp two moderately heavy dumbbells in your hands, set your feet about shoulder width apart, and stand erect with your arms running straight down at your sides, your palms toward the sides of your legs. Keep your upper arms pinned against the sides of your rib cage throughout your sets.

The Movement—Slowly curl both dumbbells straight forward and upward in semicircular arcs to your shoulders. As you raise the dumbbells, be sure to supinate your hands,

Alternate Dumbbell Curl—left arm almost finished and right arm at starting position, left; left arm at start and right arm at midpoint, right.

so your palms face upward during at least the last half of the movement. Slowly lower the weights back to the starting point, pronating your hands near the bottom of the movement.

Training Tips—You can perform Alternate Dumbbell Curls in which you lower the weight in one hand while curling the other dumbbell upward, continuing in seesaw fashion until you've completed the required number of repetitions with each arm. And you can do Dumbbell Curls while seated at the end of a flat exercise bench, curling the dumbbells simultaneously or alternately. Seated Dumbbell Curls isolate your legs from the movement, making the exercise more strict.

Incline Dumbbell Curls

Emphasis—Incline Curls stress the entire length of the biceps muscle quite intensely while giving you very little opportunity to cheat on the movement. Secondary stress is placed on the forearm flexors.

Starting Position—Grasp two moderately weighted dumbbells, sit on the seat of an incline bench, then lean back against the incline board with your arms hanging straight down from your shoulders. Your palms should be facing each other at the start of the movement.

The Movement—Slowly curl the weights simultaneously forward and upward, supinating your hands as you finish the movement. Slowly lower the weights back to the starting point, pronating your hands, and repeat the exercise for the suggested number of repetitions.

Training Tips—You needn't always curl the dumbbells upward simultaneously; you can definitely do this movement with alternate arms. Also, you needn't curl the weights directly forward on each repetition. Instead, you can curl the dumbbells somewhat out to the sides as you complete the exercise. You can also vary the angle of your incline bench, from one that is almost directly upright to an actual flat exercise bench. You will find that Lying Dumbbell Curls on a flat bench are

Cheryl Platz demonstrates Incline Dumbbell Curls—start, top; finish, bottom.

Preacher Curl—start (with EZ-Curl bar),
left; midpoint, center; finish, right.

excellent for stretching your biceps quite intensely prior to curling the dumbbells upward.

Preacher Curls

Emphasis—Preacher Curls can be performed with a barbell, two dumbbells, a single dumbbell, or a bar handle attached to a floor pulley. All variations of Preacher Curls place very strong stress on your biceps, particularly on the lower section of the muscle where it runs into the tendon that attaches to your forearm. Secondary stress is placed on the forearm flexor muscles.

Starting Position—Take an undergrip on a moderately weighted barbell with your hands set two or three inches wider than your shoulders on each side. With your arms fully bent, lean over the preacher bench with the top edge of the bench wedged beneath your armpits. Your upper arms should run down the bench parallel to each other so that your elbows are set in a somewhat more narrow position on the angled pad of the bench than the width of your grip on the bar. Slowly straighten your arms completely. Your wrists should be held straight at the start of this movement.

The Movement—Use biceps strength to slowly curl the barbell from the starting point to a finish position up against your neck beneath your chin. You can finish the movement by flexing your wrists, but be sure that you do not move your body or upper arm position as you raise or lower the weight. Slowly lower the bar back to the starting point, being sure not to bounce at the bottom position of the movement, and repeat the exercise for an appropriate number of repetitions.

Training Tips—Keeping your arms in a similar position, you can also do this movement while holding two moderately weighted dumbbells in your hands, or you can curl a dumbbell with one arm at a time. Finally, you can attach a bar handle to a cable running through a floor pulley, take a narrow undergrip on the handle, and do your Pulley Preacher Curls in this position. Incidentally, the pulley variation of this movement places a superior form of continuous tension on your working biceps muscles.

Dumbbell Preacher Curl at midpoint, left; Pulley Preacher Curl at midpoint, right.

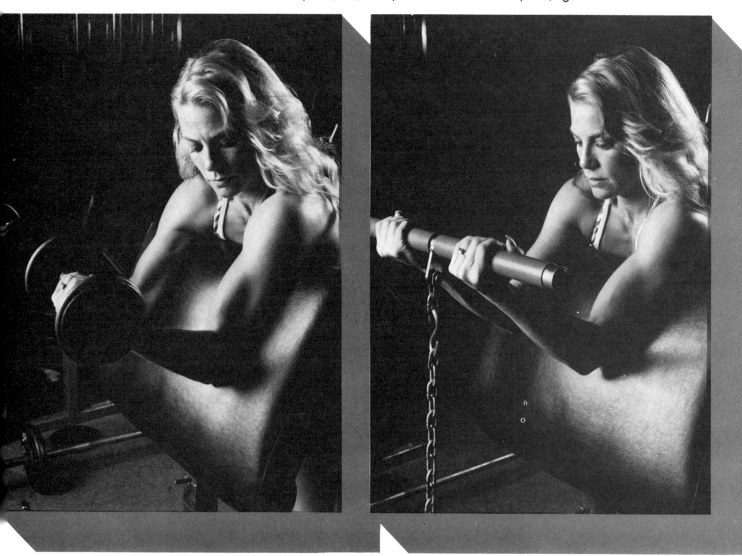

Nautilus Curls

Emphasis—Nautilus Curls place very direct stress on your biceps muscles in relative isolation from the remainder of your body. Only minimum stress is put on your forearm muscles as you do this movement.

Starting Position—Adjust the height of the machine seat to a level that will permit your arms to run comfortably up the angled pad once you sit in the seat. Run your arms up this angled pad, your elbows against the small upright pads on each side. Rest your wrists beneath the pads at the end of the machine lever arms and fully straighten your arms.

The Movement—With your wrists fully supinated, slowly bend your arms completely and curl your hands as close to your shoulders as possible. Slowly lower back to the starting point and repeat the exercise.

Training Tips—You can do Nautilus Curls with one arm at a time. You can also do them with alternating arms but in this movement you must first completely bend both arms, then keep one arm bent as you straighten and then again bend the other arm.

Nautilus Curl—start, top; finish, bottom.

Cable Curls

Emphasis—Cable Curls place direct stress on your biceps and secondary emphasis on the powerful flexor muscles of your forearms.

Starting Position—Attach a straight bar handle to the end of a cable running through a floor pulley. Take a medium-width undergrip on the bar handle, set your feet about shoulder width apart one or two feet back from the pulley, and stand erect with your arms straight and your upper arms pinned to the sides of your torso.

The Movement—Use biceps strength to slowly curl the handle from the starting posi- tion a few inches in front of your hips up to a finish point directly beneath your chin. Slowly lower the handle back to the starting point and repeat the movement for the de- sired number of repetitions.

Training Tips—A very similar movement can be performed with both hands simulta- neously while lying on your back with your feet set on either side of the pulley. Or you can attach a loop handle to the cable and perform the movement with one arm at a time. With One-Arm Cable Curls you will find it advantageous to dig your working elbow into your side and hold it there throughout your set to make the movement somewhat more strict.

Cable Curl—start, below left; finish, below right.

Dumbbell Concentration Curls

Emphasis—Concentration Curls are a very good movement for enhancing the peak on your biceps. Not every woman has the genetic potential to develop a high biceps peak, but if you have it, this exercise will bring it out.

Starting Position—Sit at the end of a flat exercise bench with your feet set about two and a half feet apart. Reach down and grasp a light dumbbell in your left hand, bracing your left elbow against the inside of your left thigh just above your knee. Fully straighten your left arm with your palm facing directly away from your left leg. You can either brace your free hand behind your working arm or place it on your right knee.

The Movement—Use biceps strength to slowly curl the dumbbell upward from the starting position to a position as close to your shoulder as possible. Be sure that you fully supinate your left hand at the top of the movement. Slowly lower the dumbbell back to the starting point and repeat the exercise. Be sure to do an equal number of sets and reps for each arm.

Training Tips—You can also do Dumbbell Concentration Curls in a standing position. With your feet set about shoulder width apart, grasp a light dumbbell in your left hand and bend forward enough to place your right hand on a bench or dumbbell rack to brace your torso at about a 45- degree angle with the floor. Fully straighten your left arm and hang it directly down from your shoulder. Be sure to keep your upper arm motionless as you do your Concentration Curls in this position.

Dumbbell Concentration Curl—start, left; finish, right.

Barbell Concentration Curl—start, left; finish, right.

Barbell Concentration Curls

Emphasis—As with Dumbbell Concentration Curls, Barbell Concentration Curls will help enhance any natural peak that your biceps have.

Starting Position—Take a narrow undergrip on the middle of a moderately weighted barbell (there should be only about six inches of space between your little fingers). With your feet set a comfortable distance apart, bend over until your torso is parallel to the floor and hang your arms straight down from your shoulders. Throughout the move-

ment your torso must remain parallel to the floor and your upper arms must be motionless.

The Movement—Use biceps strength to curl the barbell slowly in a semicircular arc from the starting position to a finish point against your throat. Slowly lower the bar back to the starting point and repeat the movement.

Training Tips—You can also do this movement lying facedown on a flat or inclined exercise bench.

Lying Barbell Triceps Extensions

Emphasis—Lying Barbell Triceps Extensions place very direct stress on the triceps, particularly on the large inner head of the muscle group.

Starting Position—Take a narrow overgrip in the middle of a moderately weighted barbell (there should be about six inches of space showing between your index fingers on the bar). Lie back on a flat bench, place your feet flat on the floor on either side of the bench to steady your body in position during the movement, and extend your arms straight up from your shoulders. Be sure to hold your upper arms motionless as you do this exercise.

The Movement—Moving only your forearms, slowly bend your arms and lower the barbell in a semicircular arc from the starting point until it lightly touches your forehead. Use triceps strength to return the barbell slowly back along the same arc to the starting point and repeat the movement.

Training Tips—You can perform a similar movement while lying back on either an incline or a decline bench rather than a flat bench. And you can do Barbell Triceps Extensions in a standing or seated position by merely extending your arms directly upward from your shoulders and restraining your upper arms from moving as you do the exercise.

Lying Barbell Triceps Extensions—start, left; finish, right.

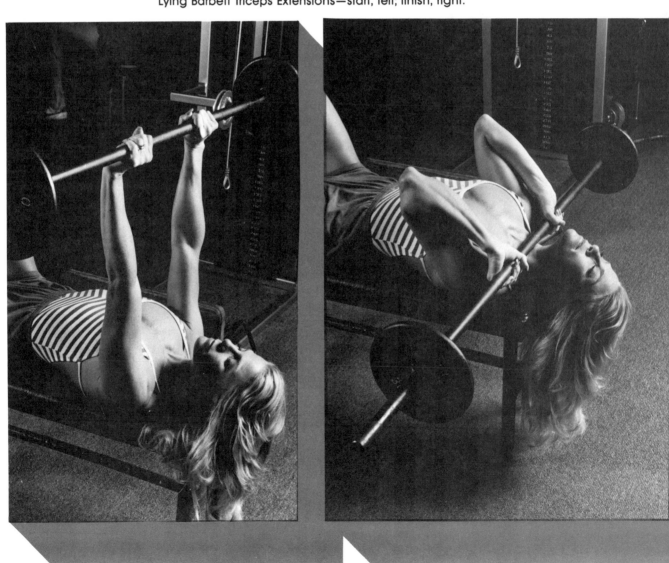

Close-Grip Bench Presses

Emphasis—Close-Grip Benches place very strong stress on your triceps (particularly the inner and outer heads of the muscle group) in conjunction with your pectorals and anterior deltoids.

Starting Position—Assume the same starting position as for Lying Barbell Triceps Extensions, except that you will use a much heavier barbell for Close-Grip Benches.

The Movement—Allowing your elbows to travel almost directly out to the sides, slowly bend your arms and lower the barbell downward until your hands touch the middle of your chest. Without bouncing the barbell off your chest, slowly push it back to straight arms' length. Repeat the exercise for the appropriate number of repetitions.

Training Tips—You can do Narrow-Grip Benches with a somewhat wider or narrower grip or on a low incline or low decline bench for somewhat different effects on your triceps muscles.

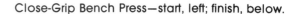

Close-Grip Bench Press—start, left; finish, below.

Dumbbell Triceps Extensions

Emphasis—Many variations of Dumbbell Triceps Extensions can be done, each placing very direct stress on your triceps muscles, particularly the long inner triceps head and the medial triceps head.

Starting Position—Place your palms flat against the inner sides of the plates of a moderately heavy dumbbell, encircling the dumbbell handle with your thumbs to keep it from slipping out of your hands. Stand erect and extend your arms directly upward so that the dumbbell handle is hanging straight downward from your hands. Keep your upper arms motionless and in near your ears as you do the movement.

The Movement—Moving just your forearms, slowly lower the dumbbell in a semicircular arc from the starting point to as low a position down your back as possible. Use triceps strength to move the dumbbell back along the same arc to the starting point and repeat the exercise.

Training Tips—You can do an identical movement seated at the end of a flat exercise bench. You can do the exercise with one arm at a time or with both arms while holding two dumbbells. The last two variations can be performed both standing and lying on a flat exercise bench.

Dumbbell Triceps Extensions—start, below left; finish, below right.

Pulley Pushdown—start, below left; finish, below right.

Pulley Pushdowns

Emphasis—Pushdowns stress the entire triceps muscle mass, but particularly the outer head of the muscle.

Starting Position—Attach a short handle with the ends angled downward to the end of an overhead pulley. With your feet set about shoulder width apart one foot back from the pulley, take a narrow overgrip on the pulley handle. Bend your arms fully, pin your elbows to the sides of your torso, and start the movement with your hands just beneath your chin. You'll probably discover that you can get more out of this exercise if you lean slightly forward at the waist as you perform the movement.

The Movement—Moving only your forearms, slowly straighten your arms. Hold this contracted position for a moment, return slowly to the starting position, and repeat the exercise.

Training Tips—You can do Pushdowns with an undergrip on the pulley handle rather than an overgrip. And you can do the movement with one arm at a time with either an overgrip or undergrip by attaching a loop handle to the end of the cable.

Pulley Extensions behind Head

Emphasis—This excellent triceps exercise stresses the entire muscle group, but particularly the long inner head of your triceps.

Starting Position—Attach the same handle as for Pushdowns to the end of a cable running through a pulley set about six or seven feet above the level of the floor. Take a narrow overgrip on the handle and face away from the machine. Bend your arms fully so your hands are at the back of your neck, bend forward at the waist, point your elbows directly forward, and place your feet forward and backward far enough away from the pulley to bear the weight of the machine.

The Movement—Slowly extend your arms completely, hold the peak contracted position for a moment, return to the starting point, and repeat the movement.

Training Tips—You can also do this exercise while kneeling on the floor and resting your elbows and forehead on a flat exercise bench. And in the standing position you can attach a loop handle to the cable and do the exercise one arm at a time, supporting the elbow of your working arm with your free hand.

Pulley Extensions behind Head—start, left; finish, right.

Nautilus Triceps Extensions

Emphasis—This is a good movement for stressing all three heads of your triceps. It's a particularly good movement for practicing peak contraction.

Starting Position—Adjust the machine's seat height so your arms run directly up the angled pad in front of your body when you sit in the seat. Place the backs of your wrists against the pads at the ends of the machine's lever arms, bend your arms completely, and sit down in the seat. Your upper arms should run directly up the angled pads with your elbows resting against the short upright pads.

The Movement—Slowly straighten your arms completely, holding the fully contracted position of the movement for a slow count of two to enhance the peak contraction effect of the exercise. Return to the starting point and repeat the movement for the suggested number of reps.

Training Tips—As with the Nautilus curling machine, you can use this exercise either one arm at a time or alternating arms.

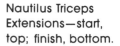

Nautilus Triceps Extensions—start, top; finish, bottom.

Dumbbell Kickbacks—start, left; finish, below.

Dumbbell Kickbacks

Emphasis—As with Nautilus Triceps Extensions, Kickbacks are a good movement for stressing all three heads of your triceps with peak contraction.

Starting Position—Grasp a light dumbbell in your left hand and stand with your right side toward a flat exercise bench. Bend over until your torso is parallel to the floor and place your right hand on the bench to steady your torso in this position during the movement. Pin your left upper arm to the side of your torso in a position parallel to the floor throughout the movement. With your palm toward your body, allow your left arm to bend at a 90-degree angle.

The Movement—Moving only your forearm, slowly straighten your arm, holding the fully contracted position for a slow count of two to emphasize the peak contraction effect of the movement in your triceps muscles. Slowly return to the starting point and repeat the movement for the suggested number of repetitions. Be sure to do an equal number of sets and reps with each arm.

Training Tips—You can do this movement with both arms simultaneously by holding two dumbbells in your hands and standing with your torso parallel to the floor. You can also do the movement with your palm facing toward the rear rather than toward your torso as you perform the exercise.

Dips between Benches

Emphasis—This is a good full-triceps exercise that emphasizes outer head development slightly more than it stresses the other two heads. Dips between Benches are often used as a finishing-off exercise in a woman bodybuilder's triceps routine.

Starting Position—Place two flat benches parallel to each other and about two and a half feet apart (you may need to adjust the distance a bit after you try the movement).

Alternatively, you can place one bench about two and a half feet back from the knee restraint bar attached to a lat machine. With your legs together, place your feet on one bench and your hands on the other bench or the restraint bar, your hands set about six inches apart and your fingers toward your feet. With your arms straight, your body will form an *L* shape when you are in the correct starting position for the exercise.

The Movement—Moving only your arms, bend your arms and slowly lower your body between the benches as far as is comfortably possible. Push back up to the starting point and repeat the movement.

Training Tips—You should experiment by placing your hands on the bench or knee restraint bar at different widths. Also, you will soon grow strong enough for added resistance in this movement, which can be applied by a training partner who either pushes down on your shoulders or places a light dumbbell in your lap as you do the exercise.

Dips between Benchs—start, top; finish, bottom.

Reverse Curls—start, left; midpoint, right; finish, opposite page.

Reverse Curls

Emphasis—Reverse Curls stress the biceps, the brachialis muscles, and the supinator muscles of your forearms.

Starting Position—Take a shoulder-width overgrip on a moderately weighted barbell, set your feet a comfortable distance apart, and stand erect with your arms running straight down at your sides and the barbell resting across your upper thighs. Press your upper arms against the sides of your torso throughout the movement.

The Movement—Use arm strength to curl the barbell slowly in a semicircular arc from your thighs to a point directly beneath your chin. Slowly lower the bar back along the same arc to the starting point and repeat the movement for the required number of reps.

Training Tips—You can do Cable Reverse Curls by attaching a straight bar handle to the end of a cable running through a floor pulley. In both the barbell and cable versions of the exercise you can also use a somewhat narrower grip than just recommended.

Barbell Wrist Curl—start (palms up), above left; finish, above right; start (palms down), below left; finish, below right.

Barbell Wrist Curls

Emphasis—Performed with your palms facing upward, this movement stresses your forearm flexor muscles; performed with your palms facing the floor, Barbell Wrist Curls stress your forearm extensor muscles.

Starting Position—Take a shoulder-width undergrip on a moderately weighted barbell. Sit at the end of a flat exercise bench with your feet set shoulder width apart and run your forearms down your thighs so your hands and wrists hang off the ends of your knees. Allow the weight in your hands to pull your fists downward as far as possible.

The Movement—Use forearm strength to curl the weight upward in a small semicircular arc as high as possible by flexing your wrists. Lower back to the starting point and repeat.

Training Tips—You can do this movement with palms down in exactly the same manner. With the palms-up grip you can have your thumbs either around the bar or under the bar as you do the movement, but your thumbs will always be around the bar in the palms-down variation. You can also do your Wrist Curls with your forearms running either lengthwise down a flat exercise bench or across the bench rather than down your thighs.

Dumbbell Wrist Curls

Emphasis—This movement is almost always performed with the palm upward to stress the flexor muscles of your forearms.

Starting Position—Grasp a moderately weighted dumbbell in your right hand, straddle a flat exercise bench, and run your forearm down the bench so your fist and wrist hang off the end of the bench with your palm upward. Allow the weight to pull your fist downward as far as possible.

The Movement—Use forearm strength to flex your wrist and curl the dumbbell upward in a tight little arc to as high a position as possible. Lower back to the starting point and repeat the movement.

Training Tips—You can also do this with both arms simultaneously, your forearms running down your thighs. However, you can get a much higher-quality contraction in your forearm muscles when you can concentrate on only one arm at a time.

Dumbbell Wrist Curl (supported)—start, left; finish, right.

Standing Barbell Wrist Curls

Emphasis—Standing Barbell Wrist Curls strongly stress the powerful flexor muscles of your forearms.

Starting Position—Place a moderately weighted barbell on a rack at about waist height. Back up to the bar and grasp it with your palms facing away from your body and your hands set slightly wider than your shoulders on each side (the bar will be behind your legs as you perform the movement). Lift the bar off the rack and stand erect with your arms straight down at your sides.

The Movement—Slowly flex your wrists to curl the barbell upward and to the rear in a small semicircular arc to as high a position as possible. Hold this peak contracted position for a moment, lower the barbell back to the starting point, and repeat the movement for the suggested number of reps.

Training Tips—A somewhat similar movement can be performed holding two dumbbells in your hands, your arms down at your sides and your palms facing toward each other. In this case you will simultaneously curl the dumbbells inward and upward in small semicircular arcs, lower back to the starting point, and repeat the movement.

Standing Barbell Wrist Curls—start, left; finish, right.

SUGGESTED ARM ROUTINES

While this book is intended primarily for intermediate and advanced weight trainers and bodybuilders, there may be a few beginners reading this chapter. We define a beginner as any woman with less than six to eight weeks of training experience behind her. Following is a beginning-level arm routine that can be used on three nonconsecutive days per week:

Exercise	Sets	Reps
Barbell Curls	3-4	8-12
Pulley Pushdowns	3-4	8-12
Barbell Wrist Curls	2-3	10-15

After you have completed six to eight weeks of the foregoing program you can move up to the following low-intermediate routine, which you can perform on three nonconsecutive days per week:

Exercise	Sets	Reps
Alternate Dumbbell Curls	3	8-12
Barbell Preacher Curls	2	8-12
Reverse Curls	2	8-12
Lying Triceps Extensions	3	8-12
Dips between Benches	3	8-12
Dumbbell Wrist Curls	3	10-15

Another six to eight weeks of training will bring you to the full intermediate level of training. At this point you can use the following arm routine on three nonconsecutive days per week:

Exercise	Sets	Reps
Seated Dumbbell Curls	3-4	8-12
Incline Curls	3	8-12
Dumbbell Concentration Curls	2-3	8-12
Cable Reverse Curls	3-4	8-12
Dumbbell Triceps Extensions	4	8-12
Behind Head Cable Extensions	3-4	8-12
Dumbbell Kickbacks	3	8-12
Standing Barbell Wrist Curls	4-5	10-15

During off-season workouts advanced bodybuilders normally follow a four-day split routine (see Chapter 10) in which they train half of their bodies on Mondays and Thursdays and the other half on Tuesdays and Fridays. Therefore, they train their arms only twice per week, which allows them to place much greater emphasis on that body part. Following is a sample off-season training program that can be used two days per week:

Exercise	Sets	Reps
Close-Grip Bench Presses	4-5	8-12
Incline Triceps Extensions	4	8-12
Pulley Pushdowns	4	8-12
Pulley Preacher Curls	4	8-12
Barbell Curls	3-4	8-12
Pulley Curls	3	8-12
Reverse Curls	3-4	8-12
Barbell Wrist Curls	4-5	10-15

ARM ROUTINES OF THE CHAMPIONS

It's important to understand that the routines presented in this section are of extremely high intensity. If you have less than a year of solid, all-out training behind you, you won't make gains using any of these programs. And it's likely that you will soon overtrain using one of these routines, which can even lead to a regression in your arm development. However, by scaling these routines down to your own ability levels, you can make good progress with them. Simply do the same exercises as your favorite champion, but perform fewer sets of each movement.

Laura Combes (American Champion)

Exercise	Sets	Reps
Close-Grip Bench Presses	3	8
Lying Triceps Extensions	3	8
Pulley Pushdowns	3	8
One-Arm Dumbbell Extensions	3	8
One-Arm Dumbell Kickbacks	3	8
Barbell Curls	3	8
Barbell Preacher Curls	3	8
Preacher Reverse Curls	3	8
Alternate Dumbbell Curls	3	8
Dumbbell Concentration Curls	3	8
Cable Curls	3	10
Barbell Wrist Curls	3	15
One-Arm Dumbbell Wrist Curls	3	8
Standing Barbell Wrist Curls	3	8

Rachel McLish.

Inger Zetterqvist (World Champion)		
Exercise	**Sets**	**Reps**
Pulley Preacher Curls	3	8–10
Seated Dumbbell Curls	2–3	8–10
Dumbbell Concentration Curls	2–3	8–10
Incline Barbell Triceps Extensions	3	8–10
Dumbell Triceps Extensions	3	8–10
Dumbell Kickbacks	2–3	10–12
Reverse Curls	3	8–10
Dumbbell Wrist Curls	3	12–15

Deborah Diana (USA Champion)		
Exercise	**Sets**	**Reps**
Parallel Bar Dips	1	10–12
Dumbbell Kickbacks	1	10–12
Lying Barbell Triceps Extensions	1	10–12
Barbell Curls	1	10–12
Alternate Dumbbell Curls	1	10–12
Reverse Curls	1	10–12
Dumbbell Wrist Curls	1	10–15

Inger Zetterqvist.

Erika Mes
(World Champion)

Exercise	Sets	Reps
Barbell Curls	4	8-10
supersetted with . . .		
Pulley Pushdowns	4	8-10
Incline Curls	3	8-10
supersetted with . . .		
Dumbbell Triceps Extensions	3	8-10
Reverse Curls	3	8-10
supersetted with . . .		
Barbell Wrist Curls	3	15

Julie McNew
(US Couples Champion)

Exercise	Sets	Reps
Close-Grip, Undergrip Chins	1	8-10
Dumbbell Concentration Curls	2	8-10
or		
Nautilus Curls	2	8-10
Parallel Bar Dips	1	8-10
Pulley Pushdowns	1	8-10
Dumbell Kickbacks	1	8-10
Nautilus Triceps Extensions	2	8-10

Cory Everson
(North American Champion)

Exercise	Sets	Reps
Dumbell Curls	4	12
Pulley Pushdowns	4	8
Pulley Curls	3	12
Lying Triceps Extensions	3	12

Sue Ann McKean
(Superbowl of Bodybuilding Champ)

Exercise	Sets	Reps
Barbell Curls	4-5	8-10
Incline Curls	4-5	8-10
Seated Dumbbell Curls	3-4	8-10
Barbell Concentration Curls	3-4	8-10
Decline Barbell Triceps Extensions	4-5	8-10
Dumbell Triceps Extensions	4-5	8-10
Pulley Pushdowns	4-5	8-10
Dumbbell Kickbacks	3-4	8-10
Cable Reverse Curls	4-5	8-10
Barbell Wrist Curls	4-5	15-20

Mary Roberts
(American Lightweight Champion)

Exercise	Sets	Reps
Alternate Dumbbell Curls	4	6-8
Preacher Curls (EZ-curl bar)	3	6-8
Barbell Curls	3	6-8
Dumbbell Concentration Curls	2-3	6-8
Lying Triceps Extensions	4	6-8
Behind Head Cable Extensions	4	6-8
Pulley Pushdowns	3-4	6-8
Barbell Wrist Curls	4	10-15

Gail Schroeder, the Western America Champion.

9
RIPPLING WAISTLINE

You can easily tell how good a woman's physical condition is merely by looking at her waistline. If there is a thick coating of fat on a woman's waistline, her physical condition is of a very low order. But if there is no visible fat and the abdominal muscles are well toned, a bodybuilder is in incredible shape.

Most champion women bodybuilders have very good abdominal development, particularly when they are peaked out for a competition. A few of the best are Rachel McLish, Carla Dunlap, Inger Zetterqvist, Laura Combes, Bev Francis, Lisser Frost-Larsen, Chris Glass, Debbie Basile, Lisa Elliott-Kolakowski, and Carolyn Cheshire.

As a competitive bodybuilder, your goal should be to develop sharply delineated abdominals. This will require a two-faceted approach of consistently intense training and a reasonably strict diet year-round. And

of these two factors, maintenance of a low-fat/low-calorie diet (see Chapter 11) is most crucial. You'll need to maintain a loose diet even in the off-season, then tighten it up just prior to a competition in order to strip away the last vestiges of body fat.

Your abdominal muscles are of supreme importance in virtually all sports, either directly or in a supporting role while other major muscle groups carry the load. Our theory of sports conditioning is that a chain is only as strong as its weakest link, so an athlete should take care to strengthen every part of her body.

Since the condition of your abdominals is an accurate barometer of your relative health and physical fitness, health- and fitness-minded women should strengthen and tone their abdominals in order to present a strong, healthy appearance. And they should maintain a diet reasonably low in calories in

139

order to avoid storing too much extra body fat around their waists.

ABDOMINAL ANATOMY AND KINESIOLOGY

You should pay attention to three primary areas of your midsection as you train your abdominals—the *rectus abdominis* (frontal abdominal wall), *obliques* (muscles at the sides of your waist), and *intercostals* (bands of muscle that run diagonally across the sides of your upper abdomen).

Your rectus abdominis has three main functions. The first of these is to help flex your torso forward toward your legs, the second is to depress your rib cage, and the third is to pull your rib cage toward your pelvis. Generally speaking, you will do variations of Sit-Ups, Leg Raises, and Crunches to strengthen and tone your rectus abdominis muscles.

The obliques located low on the sides of your waist have two primary functions. One is to twist your torso in relation to your pelvic structure; the second is to bend your torso from side to side. Of course, combinations of these two movements are also executed by your oblique muscles. The best exercises for your obliques are variations of Side Bends and Bar Twists.

Your intercostals work in combination with your obliques to twist and bend your torso to the sides as well as forward. You'll most efficiently stress your intercostals by doing Twisting Sit-Ups, Twisting Crunches, and Rope Crunches.

ABDOMINAL TRAINING SECRETS

Most champion bodybuilders believe that variety is the spice of life in training abdominals. You should include exercises for all three abdominal muscle groups in each midsection workout, and you should frequently change the order of your exercises, the exercises themselves, the number of sets, and the number of reps.

As mentioned a bit earlier in this chapter, diet plays a key role in your ability to display sharply delineated abdominals. And, even though a few bodybuilders still follow low-carbohydrate diets, it seems that the most effective fat-reduction diet is one that is low in fats and hence low in calories.

Your body has a relatively consistent number of calories that it burns each day in meeting your basic energy needs. If you consume more than this caloric maintenance level, your body will store the excess calories as fat. But if you consume less than your caloric maintenance level, your body will burn stored fat to make up the difference. And you will lose one pound of stored body fat for each 3,500-calorie deficit you create below your caloric maintenance level.

Fat is more than twice as rich a source of calories as either protein or carbohydrate. There are approximately nine calories per gram of fat, versus only four for both protein and carbohydrate. Therefore, limiting the amount of fat you consume automatically creates a caloric deficit. And the less calories you eat—as well as the more you burn up in aerobic activity—the faster you will deplete your body fat stores and reveal razor-sharp abdominals.

You will find a more detailed discussion of low-fat dieting and a sample low-fat/low-calorie diet in Chapter 11.

ABDOMINAL EXERCISES

It's essential that you correctly master each abdominal exercise described and illustrated in this section. If you don't do the movements correctly, you will receive less than optimum developmental value from them. And since it's very difficult to unlearn bad exercise habits, it's best to learn the exercises correctly from the very start of your involvement in bodybuilding training.

Sit-Ups

Emphasis—Sit-Ups are the most basic frontal abdominal exercise. Sit-Ups stress the rectus abdominis, particularly the upper half of the frontal abdominal wall. And if you perform Twisting Sit-Ups, you can also stress your intercostals.

Starting Position—Lie on your back on an abdominal board and hook your toes under the strap or roller pads provided at the foot end of the bench to restrain your legs during the movement. Bend your legs about 30 degrees to remove harmful stress from your lower back. (Performing Sit-Ups or Leg Raises with your legs held straight is potentially harmful to your lower back.) If no abdominal board is available, you can hook your toes under a heavy sofa. In either case, place your hands behind your head or neck and hold them in this position throughout your set.

The Movement—In order to perform this exercise correctly, think of it as a Curl-Up rather than as a Sit-Up. Use frontal abdominal strength to lift first your head and then your shoulders from the abdominal board. Follow through by lifting your upper back and finally the small of your back from the board, until your torso finally makes a right angle with your legs. Reverse the movement to lower yourself slowly back to the starting position and repeat the exercise for the desired number of reps.

Exercise Variations—Rather than hold your hands behind your head, you can cross your arms on your chest as you do Sit-Ups. And you can do the movement while twisting from one side to the other on succeeding reps, a movement that brings your intercostals strongly into play.

Training Tips—The best way to add to the intensity placed on your rectus abdominis group is to raise the foot end of the abdominal board incrementally. Alternatively, you can hold a loose barbell plate behind your head and neck.

Cindy Lee demonstrates Sit-Ups—start, top; finish, bottom.

Roman Chair Sit-Ups

Emphasis—As with Sit-Ups, Roman Chair Sit-Ups stress the rectus abdominis, particularly the upper half of the frontal abdominal wall. And if you perform Twisting Roman Chair Sit-Ups, you can also stress your intercostals.

Starting Position—Sit on the seat of a Roman chair facing toward the toe bar and wedge your toes beneath the bar to restrain your legs as you perform the movement. Either cross your arms over your chest or place them behind your head as you do the movement.

The Movement—Slowly move your head and shoulders to the rear until your torso is at about a 30-degree angle above a position parallel with the floor. Use frontal abdominal strength to return slowly toward the fully upright position, halting the movement just at the point where you feel stress beginning to come off your abs, usually at about a 60- to 70-degree angle above horizontal. Rock back again to the low position and repeat the exercise for the required number of reps.

Exercise Variations—As with Sit-Ups, you can do this movement twisting alternately from side to side with successive reps. Or, you can do one rep to the left, the next straight ahead, one to the right, the next straight ahead, one to the left, and so forth, until you have completed your set.

Training Tips—The easiest way to add intensity to this exercise is to place a four-by-four-inch block of wood under the foot end of the bench. Or you can use one of Rachel McLish's favorite training secrets and do the movement with pulley resistance. To use a pulley, you need to face away from the floor pulley and hold rope handles across your shoulders as you do the movement.

Roman Chair Sit-Ups—start, below; finish, right.

Leg Raises

Emphasis—Leg Raises stress the rectus abdominis, particularly the lower half of the frontal abdominal wall.

Starting Position—Lie back on an abdominal board with your head toward the upper end. Grasp the strap or roller pads in your hands to restrain your upper body during your set. Bend your legs about 15 degrees and keep them bent through the movement.

The Movement—Slowly raise your feet in a semicircular arc from the bench to a position directly above your hips. Slowly lower back to the starting point, not quite resting your heels on the board in order to keep continuous tension on your abs, and repeat the exercise for the appropriate number of reps.

Exercise Variation—You can achieve a longer range of motion in this movement if you perform Bench Leg Raises. Lie on a flat bench with your hips at the end of the bench and grasp the sides of the bench behind your head. In this position you can lower your feet well below the level of the bench at the bottom point of the movement in order to increase the range of motion of your Leg Raises.

Training Tip—To add intensity to your Leg Raises, incrementally raise the head end of the bench.

Leg Raises—start, top; finish, bottom.

Hanging Leg Raises

Emphasis—This very intense form of Leg Raises stresses the entire rectus abdominis muscle wall, particularly the lower half of the muscle group.

Starting Position—Either reach or jump up and take a shoulder-width overgrip on a chinning bar. Straighten your arms and hang your body straight down from the bar. Bend your legs slightly and keep them bent as you perform the exercise.

The Movement—Use frontal abdominal strength to raise your feet in a semicircular arc from the starting point to hip level (or until your thighs are slightly above an imaginary line parallel to the floor). Slowly lower back to the starting point and repeat the exercise for the appropriate number of repetitions.

Exercise Variations—If it's difficult for you to raise your legs high enough, you can work up to the full movement by doing Frog Kicks. In this exercise you assume the same starting position and then pull your knees up to your chest while simultaneously bending your legs fully. And while it's difficult to do Twisting Leg Raises while hanging from a chinning bar, you can easily do Twisting Frog Kicks to stimulate your intercostals along with your frontal abdominals.

Training Tip—A lot of bodybuilders experience difficulty with swinging forward and backward during a set of Hanging Leg Raises. If this is a problem for you, you can easily remedy the difficulty by having a training partner grasp your hips and hold them steady as you do the exercise.

Parallel Bar Leg Raises

Emphasis—Leg Raises performed on a set of parallel bars stress the entire frontal abdominal wall, particularly the lower half of the rectus abdominis group.

Starting Position—Jump up and support yourself on straight arms on parallel bars as if preparing to do a set of Parallel Bar Dips. Keeping your arms straight and your torso upright, bend your legs slightly and keep them bent throughout the movement.

The Movement—Slowly raise your feet in a semicircular arc from the starting point to a position slightly above the level of your hips in front of you. Lower back to the starting point and continue the set until you have done the number of repetitions suggested in your training program.

Exercise Variation—A less intense movement similar to Frog Kicks can be done in this position. Simply assume the starting position for Parallel Bar Leg Raises and then simultaneously bend your legs fully and pull your knees up to your chest.

Training Tip—Many gyms have an apparatus for this movement in which you rest your weight on your elbows and forearms, which in turn rest on pads set parallel to each other and high enough off the floor to allow the complete movement.

Candy Csencsits demonstrates Hanging Leg Raises.

Parallel Bar Leg Raises—
start, top; finish, bottom.

Knee-Ups—start, left; finish, below.

Knee-Ups

Emphasis—This frontal abdominal movement of relatively low intensity particularly stresses the lower half of your rectus abdominis wall.

Starting Position—Sit at one end of a moderately high flat exercise bench. Incline your torso backward until it is at a 45-degree angle to the floor and grasp the sides of the bench to maintain this torso position as you do the exercise. Straighten your legs and move them to a position in which they make one long line with your torso. Ideally, your heels will be just clear of the floor in this position.

The Movement—Simultaneously bend your legs completely and pull your knees up to touch your chest. Hold this peak contracted top position for a moment, return to the starting point, and repeat the exercise.

Exercise Variation—You can do this movement pulling your legs upward a little to each side, preferably while also twisting your legs to the same side on alternating repetitions.

Crunches

Emphasis—Crunches are one of the best frontal abdominal movements. Crunches stress the entire rectus abdominis wall, from your rib cage right down to your pelvis.

Starting Position—Lie on your back on the gym floor with your lower legs resting lightly over a flat exercise bench. In this position your thighs will be perpendicular to the floor and your shins will be parallel to the floor. Place your hands behind your head and neck and keep them in this position throughout the movement.

The Movement—In order to perform this exercise correctly you must simultaneously accomplish four tasks: (1) use upper abdominal strength to lift your head and shoulders from the floor; (2) use lower abdominal strength to lift your hips from the floor; (3) use the power of your frontal abs to force your rib cage toward your pelvis; and (4) forcefully blow out all of your air. When you do these movements correctly you will feel a very intense contraction in your frontal abs. Hold this peak contracted position for a moment, return to the starting point, and repeat the exercise.

Exercise Variations—A very similar movement can be performed while resting your feet on a wall with your legs in the same position as for Crunches across a bench. And you can do L Crunches with your legs running straight up a wall and your tush in the corner formed by the wall and floor.

Crunches—start, top; finish, bottom.

Rope Crunches—start, left; finish, below.

Rope Crunches

Emphasis—This is a good all-around abdominal exercise, particularly when used at the conclusion of a midsection routine. Rope Crunches place intense stress on the rectus abdominis, intercostal, and serratus muscles. Secondary stress is placed on the lower lats and (if done in a twisting manner) the obliques.

Starting Position—Attach a rope handle to a high pulley and grasp the two ends of the handle with your palms facing each other. Step about two feet back from the pulley (you should be facing the weight stack) and kneel down on the gym floor. With your arms held relatively straight, extend your body directly toward the pulley.

The Movement—In order to perform this exercise correctly you must simultaneously accomplish four tasks: (1) bend forward at the waist and touch your forehead to the floor directly in front of you; (2) do a "Mini-Pullover" movement with your arms to touch your hands to the floor directly in front of your head; (3) forcefully blow out all of your air; and (4) consciously tense all of the muscles on the front of your abdomen.

Exercise Variations—You can do Rope Crunches twisting alternately from side to side with each succeeding rep. Or you can do the movement with one hand at a time holding the rope handle, a variation that puts terrific stress on the intercostals on the side of your body with the hand gripping the handle.

Bar Twists

Emphasis—This exercise stresses the rotational aspect of your oblique muscles at the sides of your waist. You will find that various twisting movements also help loosen up your lower back.

Starting Position—Place a broomstick or an unloaded barbell across your shoulders and wrap your arms around it to restrain them. Stand erect with your feet set shoulder

Bar Twisting to the left, then to the right.

Seated Twisting to the right, then to the left.

width apart and your toes pointed directly forward.

The Movement—Keeping your hips motionless, forcefully twist your torso as far to the left as possible, then immediately as far to the right as possible. Twist rhythmically back and forth between these two extremes until you have done the suggested number of repetitions to each side.

Exercise Variations—One easy way to keep your hips from moving as you do this movement (and avoid negating much of the value of the exercise) is to do it seated on a flat exercise bench with your legs intertwined in the legs of the bench in order to keep your lower body motionless. You can also perform Bent Twists, in which you stand with your feet about shoulder width apart and hold your torso parallel to the floor as you do the exercise.

Side Bends

Emphasis—Side Bends stress the trunk flexion aspect of your oblique muscles.

Starting Position—Place a light barbell across your shoulders behind your neck and grasp the ends of the bar out near the collars. Set your feet a bit narrower than shoulder width apart and stand erect.

The Movement—Bend directly to the right as far as is comfortably possible. Recover to the starting point and then bend as far as you can to the left. Continue bending rhythmically from one side to the other until you have finished doing the required number of repetitions to each side.

Comment—The obliques grow in mass relatively easily, so it's best to use relatively light weights in this exercise and concentrate on doing high reps (50 or more).

Side Bends to the right, then to the left.

Seated Side Bend (below) to the left.

SUGGESTED ABDOMINAL ROUTINES

While this book is intended primarily for intermediate and advanced weight trainers and bodybuilders, there may be a few beginners reading this chapter. We define a beginner as any woman with less than six to eight weeks of steady training behind her. Following is a beginning-level abdominal routine that can be used three nonconsecutive days per week:

Exercise	Sets	Reps
Sit-Ups	2	20–30
Leg Raises	2	20–30
Seated Twisting	2	25

After you have completed six to eight weeks on the foregoing program you can move up to the following low-intermediate routine, which you can perform three nonconsecutive days per week as a giant set:

Exercise	Sets	Reps
Roman Chair Sit-Ups	2–3	20–30
Bench Leg Raises	2–3	20–30
Seated Twisting	2–3	25–30
Crunches	2–3	15–20

Another six to eight weeks of training will bring you to the full intermediate level of training. At that point you can use the following abdominal routine four days per week as a giant set:

Exercise	Sets	Reps
Incline Sit-Ups	3	10–15
Incline Leg Raises	3	10–15
Side Bends	3	25–30
Roman Chair Sit-Ups	3	25–30
Seated Twisting	3	25–30
Crunches	3	20–25

ABDOMINAL ROUTINES OF THE CHAMPIONS

It's important to understand that the routines presented in this section are of extremely high intensity. If you have less than a year of solid, all-out training behind you, you won't make good gains using any of these programs. And it's likely that you will soon overtrain using one of these routines, which can even lead to a regression in your physical development. However, by scaling these routines down to your own ability levels, you *can* make good progress on them. Simply do the same exercises as your favorite champion, but perform fewer sets of each movement.

Laura Combes
(American Champion)

Exercise	Sets	Reps
Hanging Leg Raises	4–5	15
Twisting Roman Chair Sit-Ups	4–5	30
Side Bends	4–5	50
Bench Leg Raises	4–5	30
Crunches	4–5	30

This routine is performed as a giant set.

Lynn Conkwright
(Pro World Champion)

Exercise	Sets	Reps
Wall Crunches	3	20–25
Hanging Leg Raises	3	15–20
Jackknife Crunches	3	20–25
Cable Crunches	3	20–25
Seated Twisting	3	25

Lisa Elliott-Kolakowski
(Gold's Classic Champ)

Exercise	Sets	Reps
Incline Sit-Ups	3–4	20–25
Incline Leg Raises	3–4	20–25
Crunches	3–4	20–25
Side Bends	3–4	20–25
Roman Chair Sit-Ups	3–4	25–30

This routine is performed as a giant set.

Sonee Baumgarten

Stella Martinez
(Ms. USA)

Exercise	Sets	Reps
Hanging Leg Raises	3	15–20
supersetted with . . .		
Incline Sit-Ups	3	20–30
Incline Leg Raises	3	20–30
supersetted with . . .		
Wall Crunches	3	20–30
Bench Leg Raises	3	20–30
supersetted with . . .		
Cable Crunches	3	20–25

Sue Ann McKean
(Superbowl of Bodybuilding Champ)

Exercise	Sets	Reps
Hanging Leg Raises	3–4	15–20
Roman Chair Sit-Ups	3–4	25–30
Side Bends	3–4	30
Parallel Bar Leg Raises	3–4	20–25
L Crunches	3–4	20–25

This routine is performed as a giant set.

Inger Zetterqvist
(World Champion)

Exercise	Sets	Reps
Incline Sit-Ups	2–3	20–25
Bench Leg Raises	2–3	20–25
Crunches (Twisting)	2–3	20–25

This routine is performed as a triset.

Carolyn Cheshire at the 1982 Miss Olympia.

10
ADVANCED TRAINING PRINCIPLES

With six months to a year of steady, high-intensity training under your belt, you can properly be called an advanced bodybuilder. And at this point you must choose to specialize in one of the several areas of weight training. This book is intended primarily for women who wish to enter bodybuilding competition, but you can also specialize in powerlifting, weight training for athletic conditioning, or resistance workouts for improved physical fitness, or you can merely continue with a relatively high intensity of weight workouts to improve your appearance, health, and general fitness.

Regardless of which area you choose for specialized work, we will applaud your decision and offer our encouragement to continue hard weight training using the suggestions included in this book. However, we speak here primarily to bodybuilders, and the information presented in this chapter is intended specifically to bridge the gap between normal high-intensity weight training and true bodybuilding workouts.

Topics discussed in this chapter include how to develop training instinct, stress management, flexibility training, individualizing your routines, holistic sets, split and double-split routines, muscle confusion workouts, peak contraction, continuous tension, staggered sets, bodybuilding drugs, and the optimum approach to bodybuilding psychology.

TRAINING INSTINCT

While all of the Weider Training Principles lend structure to bodybuilding training, not a single principle works precisely the same for any two bodybuilders. It's an inevitable fact that every woman's body—and the way in which it reacts to exercise—is as totally unique as her fingerprints. So while we can give you instructions, exercises, and training routines that will cause your body to respond in a general way, only you can evaluate the precise response your body makes to each stimulus and the relative worth of each technique.

Your tool for making these evaluations is the Weider Instinctive Training Principle. Instinctive training ability merely involves being able to recognize the biofeedback signals that your body is constantly giving you, interpret the meaning of each signal, and apply the data you have learned to make valuable adjustments in your overall training philosophy. It takes only a few months to master the Weider Instinctive Training Principle, but once mastered it is one of the most valuable bodybuilding tools at your disposal!

What is biofeedback? One of the simplest examples is the sensation of hunger, which is your body's way of telling you that it needs to be fed. You've no doubt become accustomed to interpreting such biofeedback signals as hunger, thirst, sleepiness, fatigue, irritability, pain, and so forth, but you probably haven't paid any attention to bodybuilding-oriented biofeedback. And if you did consciously seek out bodybuilding biofeedback, you would soon be a master of the Weider Instinctive Training Principle.

The most common form of biofeedback that a champion bodybuilder looks for is a good muscle pump, that tight blood-congested sensation in a muscle group that tells you the muscle has been trained optimally. An even more immediate signal of optimum training is the deep fatigue burn in a muscle that builds up toward the end of an all-out set. And a somewhat less immediate indication of a great workout is the mild next-day soreness in a muscle group that is a sure indication you have worked it harder than ever before.

Following is a variety of other biofeedback signals that should be a good indication that you're making excellent progress from your training.

- training poundages that gradually increase in each exercise
- a level of enthusiasm for training that makes you look forward to each new workout
- the ability to feel your muscle contractions forcefully in every repetition of each exercise
- high energy levels
- increased muscle mass and/or muscle density
- generally decreased (or unchanged) levels of body fat
- a healthy appetite
- an ability to stay relaxed and sleep well

On the other hand, there are eight pieces of negative biofeedback of which you should also be aware, for they are good indications that you are beginning to enter an overtrained state that will most surely halt your progress. Following are the negative feedback signals that you should monitor:

- lack of progress
- chronic fatigue
- lack of enthusiasm for workouts
- chronically sore joints and/or muscles
- loss of appetite
- insomnia
- irritability
- elevated morning pulse rate

Make Experiments

Once you have mastered instinctive training ability, you'll make it to the top as a bodybuilder only if you use your body as a laboratory, make literally hundreds of experiments in it, and use your instinctive training ability to evaluate the results of these experiments.

Inger Zetterqvist (World Champion) explains: "There's no question that I've been genetically gifted for bodybuilding, but genetics aren't the reason why I made it to the top so quickly. Rather, it was my ability to experiment with literally hundreds of combinations of training principles, exercises, routines, and diets and correctly evaluate the worth of each variable to my own body. This allowed me to take a superhighway to success rather than wandering down a country lane with many unproductive cul de sacs along the way."

Erika Mes (World Champion) agrees with

Inger Zetterqvist.

Inger: "Even though I've now won the IFBB World Championship, I'm still constantly experimenting with new training and dietary variables. Living in Holland, much of my new information comes from reading *Muscle & Fitness* magazine each month, but I think that I got more information in a shorter period of time one spring when I spent two months training at Gold's Gym in California. That experience gave me scores of new things with which to experiment, which ultimately has greatly improved my physique. Need I say more?"

To conclude this section on instinctive training, let's listen to **Deborah Diana** (Ms. USA and winner of more than 20 titles): "Once you get a good instinct for bodybuilding, it shouldn't take you more than two or three workouts in order to determine which new technique is working well for your body. Actually, after six years of competition I've mastered instinctive training to the point where I can now tell after only a single workout if something is working for me, simply by the feel I get in the working muscles as I try out the new stimulus."

STRESS MANAGEMENT

Stress is one of the most pervasively destructive factors in modern life, and you can greatly accelerate your bodybuilding progress if you can learn to minimize the amount of stress you bear in your everyday life. It's not particularly difficult to reduce the amount of stress in your life.

The late Dr. Hans Selye was the world's leading stress researcher, and he identified two types of stress—*distress*, or negative stress, and *eustress*, or positive stress. And the trick, according to Dr. Selye, is to minimize distress and maximize eustress.

Common forms of distress are life-threatening situations, money problems, sudden loud noises, family difficulties, unfriendly co-workers, and lack of sleep. And common forms of eustress are mountain hiking, skydiving, fishing, hunting and—lo, and behold—bodybuilding training.

In order to reduce distress in your life, you must first take pencil and paper in hand and list those things in your life that you find unpleasant. Within a few days you should have quite a list of distressful situations. Then you must devise a plan to systematically avoid as many of these stressful situations as possible. Even if you can eliminate only a third or a half of the distressful situations on your list, you will have made giant strides in improving your physique by successfully managing stress in your life.

On the other hand, bodybuilding training and virtually all other physical activities are eustressful and should be encouraged. The inclusion of a satisfying hobby can also be eustressful. This hobby can range from sedentary to physical and should be governed only by your personal interests in life. However, you should choose a hobby that you can engage in on a regular basis, at least once or twice per week.

Distress will hold back your progress as a bodybuilder because it prevents proper recuperation between workouts. So, by minimizing distress in your life and maximizing eustress, you will be taking significant steps to improve your progress as a bodybuilder.

FLEXIBILITY TRAINING

In bodybuilding you gain the best quality of muscle development by performing each exercise over the fullest possible range of motion. Most women bodybuilders are careful to contract their muscles completely in the finish position of every exercise, but they are lax in stretching their muscles in the bottom range of each movement. Therefore, engaging in regular flexibility training can be quite valuable in improving your overall physical development.

Stretching also helps prevent injuries, particularly when you are training with extremely heavy weights. And proper stretching is both a very good warm-up activity and a profitable warm-down practice. Postworkout stretching has been shown by the Weider Research Clinic to be especially valuable for reducing day-after muscle soreness when you have been training with maximum intensity.

While there are forms of stretching that advocate bouncing movements or stretching in which a partner pushes you forcefully into the stretched position, we have concluded after long research that it's best to stretch in a gentle manner. With each stretching exercise you should move your body slowly into the stretched position until you reach the point where you begin to feel pain in the muscles being stretched. Then you should back off a degree or two and hold this position for 30–60 seconds to attain maximum benefit from the stretch.

Within the scope of this book it would be impossible to present a more complete discussion of flexibility training than has already been published in an earlier volume of the Weider muscle library. It is a chapter called "Stretching Exercises for Fitness" by Bill Reynolds in one of our "*The Best of Joe Weider's* Muscle & Fitness" anthologies, *More Training Tips and Routines* (Contemporary Books, 1982).

INDIVIDUALIZED ROUTINES

It's definitely possible for you to follow the

routines presented in this and similar books, as well as in the host of bodybuilding magazines currently published, for as long as you continue to lift weights. However, you won't get nearly as much out of this practice as you would if you learned how to make up your own individualized training programs.

The first rule that you should follow in formulating your own workouts is to use the Weider Muscle Priority Training Principle. This principle advocates scheduling exercise for your weaker muscle groups early in your workout when you have maximum physical and mental energy to devote to training the weak body part with optimum intensity. And conversely, this principle suggests that you should train your stronger muscle groups both with less intensity and later in your workouts. The ultimate goal of muscle priority training is to balance your physical proportions, and it will do the job quite well if you assiduously follow it.

Past the Weider Muscle Priority Training Principle, you should generally train your larger muscle groups (e.g., thighs, chest, back) earlier in your routines than the smaller body parts. Large muscle groups require great expenditures of energy when they are trained, and you will quickly find that it's easier to do a good biceps workout than five or six sets of Squats when your energy reserves are low. Therefore, it's always best to save your smaller muscle groups until toward the end of your workout.

Furthermore, you should always do your torso exercises prior to your arm work. Your chest, back, and shoulder muscles are far larger and stronger than your biceps and triceps. As a result, your arm muscles virtually always grow too fatigued to continue a Bench Press, Military Press, or Barbell Row exercise to the point where you would truly be able to push your torso groups to the limit. This is a bad situation that can be made even worse if you make the mistake of training your arms first and further weakening them in relation to your chest, back, and shoulder muscles.

As you formulate training programs for each muscle group, you should include both basic and isolation movements. Basic exercises are included to build mass, and you should do a greater proportion of basic movements during an off-season training cycle. In contrast, isolation exercises are intended to shape and add detail to each muscle group, and you should include a greater proportion of isolation movements during a precontest peaking phase.

Finally, you should be conservative in the number of total sets that you perform for each body part. During an off-season cycle, we suggest no more than 12–15 total sets for large, more complex muscle groups (thighs, back, chest, and shoulders) and no more than 8–10 total sets for smaller body parts. And prior to a competition, you can safely do 20–25 percent more total sets for each muscle group.

HOLISTIC SETS

The idea behind the Weider Holistic Sets Training Principle is that different numbers of reps in each set result in different types of muscle and strength development. For example, you've no doubt noticed that low reps (four to six) are best for building a great degree of muscle mass and considerable strength, while high reps (more than 15) are best for increasing muscular endurance and peaking out physique definition.

With holistic sets, then, we suggest that you follow a pattern in which you begin an exercise with a light weight for about 15 reps. Then, with each succeeding set, you increase the weight that you are using and drop the reps a bit, typically from 15 to 12, 10, 8, 6, 4, and perhaps even as low as one or two. Then, to finish off your exercise, you should do two or three pump sets of higher reps with lighter weights. For example, you might do one pump set of 10 reps with a somewhat lighter weight, followed by a final pump set of 15 reps with an even lighter weight.

With holistic sets you will make very good gains in muscle mass and quality, which is the reason we recommend them quite highly for at least one basic exercise per body part, particularly in the off-season.

SPLIT AND DOUBLE-SPLIT ROUTINES

"Once you get to the point where it takes you more than an hour and a half to complete your full-body workout," reveals **Stacey Bentley** (Zane Pro Invitational Champion), "it's time to begin following a split routine in which you work only part of your body each day. The simplest form of split routine involves training half of your body on Mondays and Thursdays, the other half on Tuesdays and Fridays, perhaps stressing your calves and abdominals each of the four training days."

In Figure 10–1 you will find two alternative examples of the type of four-day split routine that Stacey Bentley is talking about.

Choice 1

Mon-Thu	Tue-Fri
Abdominals	Abdominals
Chest	Thighs
Back	Upper Arms
Shoulders	Forearms
Calves	Calves

Choice 2

Mon-Thu	Tue-Fri
Abdominals	Abdominals
Chest	Thighs
Shoulders	Back
Triceps	Forearms
Biceps	Neck
Calves	Calves

Figure 10-1: Examples of Four-Day Split Routines.

"After several months of using a four-day split routine," notes **Stella Martinez** (Ms. USA), "you can move up in training intensity by following a five-day split routine. In a five-day split you will still divide up your body parts into two equal groups, as for a four-day split, but you will train half of your body on Monday, Wednesday, and Friday the first week and on Tuesday and Thursday the sec-

ond week. Of course the first week you'll train the second half on Tuesday and Thursday, while on the second week you hit it on Monday, Wednesday, and Friday. In this way, over a two-week period of time, you will give the same amount of work to each muscle group."

You will find an example of a five-day split routine in Figure 10–2.

	M	T	W	T	F
Week 1	A	B	A	B	A
Week 2	B	A	B	A	B
Week 3	A	B	A	B	A
Week 4	B	A	B	A	B
Week 5	A	B	A	B	A

A = first half of the body.
B = second half of the body.

Figure 10-2: Example of a Five-Day Split Routine.

"While many women bodybuilders follow a four-day split routine in the off-season, virtually all of them use a six-day split prior to a show," explains **Rachel McLish** (Miss Olympia). "There are two types of six-day split routines, one in which each major muscle group is trained twice per week and another in which each major body part is worked three times per week. The second type of six-day split routine is much more intense than the first type."

Some of the most experienced women bodybuilders, those with superior recuperative abilities, are able to use a six-day split routine year-round, working each major muscle group twice per week in the off-season and hitting each large body part three times per week prior to a competition. Generally speaking, the more frequently you train each muscle group prior to a competition, the more muscular you'll eventually be onstage at your show.

In Figure 10–3 you will find examples of both types of six-day split routines.

Each Muscle Group Twice per Week

Mon-Thu	Tue-Fri	Wed-Sat
Abdominals	Abdominals	Abdominals
Chest	Thighs	Shoulders
Back	Forearms	Upper Arms
Calves	Neck	Calves

Each Muscle Group Three Times per Week

Mon-Wed-Fri	Tue-Thu-Sat
Abdominals	Abdominals
Thighs	Chest
Lower Back	Upper Back
Calves	Shoulders
Forearms	Upper Arms

Figure 10-3: Examples of Six-Day Split Routines.

Only a few experienced women bodybuilders can use the Weider Double-Split System Training Principle. This principle involves performing two workouts each training day, six days per week. In the most simple form of double-split routine you will stress your major muscle groups in normal six-day-per-week fashion early in the day, then come back at night to do your workout for your abdominals, forearms, and calves.

In the next most intense form of double-split routine you will work out twice per day three days per week and only once on the other three training days. An example of this type of modified double-split routine is presented in Figure 10-4.

Mon-Wed-Fri (A.M.)	Mon-Wed-Fri (P.M.)	Tue-Thu-Sat (A.M. or P.M.)
Abdominals	Calves	Abdominals
Thighs	Back	Shoulders
Chest	Forearms	Biceps
		Triceps

Figure 10-4: Modified Double-Split Routine

The final step up the ladder of training frequency is a full double-split routine in which you train twice per day six days each week, resting only on Sundays. An example of this type of full double-split routine is presented in Figure 10-5.

Mon-Wed-Fri (A.M.)	Mon-Wed-Fri (P.M.)
Abdominals	Calves
Chest	Shoulders
Forearms	Triceps

Tue-Thu-Sat (A.M.)	Tue-Thu-Sat (P.M.)
Abdominals	Back
Thighs	Biceps

Figure 10-5: Full Double-Split Routine.

Reviewing split and double-split routines, keep in mind that more frequent training tends to stimulate your basal metabolic rate, burning off fat and making you more cut-appearing as a competition arrives. As a result, most bodybuilders who have little difficulty in achieving peak muscularity are the ones who gradually do more total workouts each week as a competition approaches. This system includes both an increased number of actual weight workouts and an added number of aerobic training sessions. Prior to a major championship many women are training three or four times per day, and their muscularity is incredible!

MUSCLE CONFUSION

"One of the most marvelous physiological factors in bodybuilding is the great adaptability of a woman's body to heavy exercise," explains **Lisa Elliott-Kolakowski** (Ms. Eastern America and a Gold's Classic Champion). "When we place a heavier-than-normal resistance on a muscle group it adapts by growing a little larger and stronger so it can more easily lift that same weight the next time it's forced to.

"Unfortunately, the body not only adapts to exercise, it seeks an area of what could be called 'comfort' in which it doesn't necessarily have to keep adapting. This usually occurs in terms of the actual bodybuilding routine that we follow rather than within each exercise. And that's the reason we are encouraged to switch to a new training program each four to six weeks.

"I personally switch my routines each four to six weeks, but there are top bodybuilders who can stay on the same type of program seemingly for life. This type of woman tends to be stoic, methodical, and not easily bored. And when such a woman discovers what works well for her individual body she will tend to stick to the program that works for her for a long period of time.

"On the other hand, there are excitable, easily bored women who grow so used to a particular routine in such a short time that they would make little progress if they didn't switch to a new training program during virtually every workout. Usually, this type of woman's body doesn't adapt that quickly to a workout, but her mind does, and the mind is so powerful that it must have a new routine at almost every workout."

A bodybuilder who uses a new routine every time she works out is using the Weider Muscle Confusion Training Principle. Muscle confusion needn't mean that you must completely change your routine for each workout. Instead, you could simply change the angles of many of your exercises, such as doing Incline Dumbbell Presses on a 30-degree incline bench one day and on a 45-degree bench the next.

Other variables that you can try in your workouts are changing the tempo of your workout, doing higher or lower sets, performing higher or lower reps, doing different body parts than you normally do on some workout days, using more or fewer forced reps (and other Weider Intensification Training Principles), and occasionally even skipping a workout.

PEAK CONTRACTION

In order to understand the Weider Peak Contraction Training Principle you must first understand the anatomy and physiology of muscle contraction. The most basic compo-

nent of a muscle is a muscle cell. Thousands of muscle cells are strung together end to end to form muscle fibers, and hundreds of fibers are bundled together to form an actual skeletal muscle that you can contract against a weight.

When a muscle contracts it shortens in order to move the bone or bones to which it's attached. But when you contract a muscle it's important to understand that each muscle cell contracts (shortens) either completely or not at all. This is a phenomenon that exercise physiologists call the "all or nothing" model of muscle contraction. You must also realize that more and more muscle cells are contracted in order to shorten a muscle to its minimum possible length.

Consider that you have the maximum possible number of individual muscle cells contracted when you have a muscle group completely flexed; it just stands to reason that you should place a heavy load on the working muscle in this position. And when you do so you strongly stimulate the muscles to grow in mass, quality, and strength, the very basis of the Weider Peak Contraction Training Principle.

Unfortunately, a large number of exercises place little or no stress on fully contracted muscles. "The Standing Barbell Curl is a good example of an exercise that runs counter to the Peak Contraction Principle," notes **Kay Baxter** (Gold's Classic Champion). "When you have curled the barbell all the way up to your chin your biceps are fully flexed. But in that position they bear absolutely none of the weight of the bar. Instead, your anterior and medial deltoids are taking up most of the stress.

"To place peak contraction stress on your biceps you would be better off doing Barbell Concentration Curls, bent over with your torso parallel to the floor. Hold the top position of the movement for a slow count of two to enhance the peak contraction effect of the movement."

Most machine exercises place heavy stress on the muscles in their peak contracted position. A few of these are Leg Extensions, Leg Curls, Lat Pulldowns, Pulley Rows, Chins,

Kay Baxter.

Pec Deck Flyes, and Machine Curls. There are also quite a few free-weight movements that apply peak contraction to the muscles, including Dumbbell Concentration Curls, Barbell Bent Rows, Front Raises, Side Laterals, Bent Laterals, Dumbbell Kickbacks, and One-Leg Calf Raises performed while holding a dumbbell in one hand.

Unlike some Weider Training Principles, peak contraction is appropriate for use in both off-season and precontest training cycles. Peak contraction develops both a high degree of muscle mass and a fine type of muscle quality, so you should always include several peak contraction exercises in all of your routines.

CONTINUOUS TENSION

When you move a weight too quickly over its full range of motion a momentum is built up that robs your working muscles of much of the stress they should receive from the exercise. As a result, the Weider Slow, Continuous Tension Training Principle was evolved to prevent momentum from robbing your muscles of some of the resistance they should receive. With this principle you will seek to move the weight in any exercise slowly over every millimeter of its range of motion. And at the same time you build as much tension as possible into both the working muscles and those muscles antagonistic to the working muscles.

"Continuous tension sets are murder," exclaims **Chris Glass** (Los Angeles Champion), "especially when you use them in conjunction with peak contraction during a peaking cycle. The amount of weight that you can use in each exercise is reduced drastically, but the lighter weight can be made to feel like a ton! I firmly believe that this combination of peak contraction and continuous tension is largely responsible for the progress I've made recently in etching better striations into my muscles."

STAGGERED SETS

The closer you come to a competition, the more total sets of abdominal (and sometimes calf) work you will perform in order to reach an optimum peak. And when you're doing 15–20 sets of ab training you can grow very fatigued with the entire process. However, there is a way in which you can make all of this abdominal work far less boring. This is the Weider Staggered Sets Training Principle.

With staggered sets you insert a set of abdominal work between every two or three sets of training for some other major body part. For example, you may be doing four sets each of Seated Pulley Rows, Front Lat Pulldowns, One-Arm Dumbbell Bent Rows, and Stiff-Arm Pulldowns for your back. So after the first two sets of Pulley Rows you interset a set of Hanging Leg Raises. Two more sets of Pulley Rows are followed by another set of Hanging Leg Raises, two sets of Pulldowns by a set of Hanging Leg Raises, two more sets of Pulldowns by a set of Crunches, and so forth, until you've essentially performed your entire normally boring abdominal program without realizing it.

One common worry with the Weider Staggered Sets Training Principle is that the abdominal work intersetted between training for other body parts will slow the momentum of your workout for the major muscle group. Nothing could be further from the truth. Investigation at the Weider Research Clinic has demonstrated beyond a shadow of a doubt that occasionally intersetting abdominal training between sets for major muscle groups actually has a beneficial effect on the recovery of the major body part, thus making it easier to stress it to the limit in a subsequent set.

THE DRUG QUESTION

Virtually all champion women bodybuilders, the IFBB, and AFWB, and ourselves are firmly opposed to the use of drugs that could potentially enhance a woman's physical development. These drugs primarily consist of anabolic steroids, thyroid drugs, appetite depressants, and energy stimulants. And, in the words of Rachel McLish, "Drugs are ruining the sport of women's bodybuilding!"

There are two valid arguments against the use of bodybuilding drugs. The first of these is one of ethics and morality. Is it fair to introduce an unnatural substance into your body in order to gain an edge over a competitor? And, if so, where will it all stop? If something isn't done to halt drug usage in the sport, bodybuilding champions of the future will probably be those women with the best physicians and pharmacists rather than athletes who have trained the hardest and dieted the most strictly.

Secondly, all bodybuilding drugs have potentially disastrous side effects. Anabolic steroids, which are artificial male hormones, can masculinize a woman's body, deepening her voice, enlarging her clitoris, and leading to a greatly increased growth of body hair. There is also plenty of evidence that steroids can actually cause cancer. As a result, beginning in 1984, the IFBB will be testing for steroids and other bodybuilding drugs at all international competitions as well as at selected national-level events.

Regardless of what you hear about the "benefits" of taking certain bodybuilding drugs, we implore you to turn away from their use. In the long run they can greatly harm your body as well as the sport of bodybuilding.

THE BODYBUILDING MIND

Above all else, a champion bodybuilder's mental approach to her sport is *positive*. And in a world filled with negative stimuli it's no mean feat to maintain a completely positive frame of mind in bodybuilding. The secret is to begin looking for negative thoughts about bodybuilding, then systematically cast them out of your mind, replacing them with positive stimuli. After several months of consciously playing down the negative and emphasizing the positive, you will have a predominantly positive mental attitude toward your bodybuilding.

Next, you should practice concentrating on each rep of every exercise that you perform in your workouts. Focus your mind as completely as possible on your muscles' powerfully flexing and then extending under the load you are putting on them. And the stronger you can make this mind-to-muscle link, the more you'll get out of your workout.

We can give you a good exercise that will improve your ability to concentrate. Lie on your back in a comfortable position in as quiet a room as possible. Listen to your breathing pattern, exhaling and inhaling. Concentrate only on your breathing, allowing nothing else to intrude on your concentration. Begin counting your breaths, stopping only when you are distracted from concentrating solely on your breathing and

counting process. At first you may not even get up to five before you're distracted, but eventually you'll be able to concentrate on 100 or more consecutive breaths. At that point you will have superior concentrative abilities.

The last mental conditioning technique that we'd like to teach you is called *visualization*. Visualization is a simple process by which you can program your subconscious mind—which in many ways is more powerful than your conscious mind—to help you achieve your goals.

Visualization is a conscious application of a process that psychologists call *self-actualization*. In this process you might fantasize about becoming a doctor, then spend so much time thinking about being a physician that your subconscious mind begins to make choices that make it easy to become a doctor. Instead of balking at attending an anatomy lab, you find yourself anxious to get off to the lab.

In bodybuilding visualization you can daydream about the type of incredible physique you soon wish to have, and this programs your subconscious mind to make it easier to train and diet. However, this type of visualization practice takes into consideration only the imagined sense of sight. What if you could involve your other four senses—hearing, touch, taste, and smell? The answer to this question is that the more senses you can include in your visualization process, the more you'll get out of it in terms of building an incredibly improved physique.

So, in addition to seeing your physique the way you'd like it to become one day, why not also feel yourself walking around inside it? Listen in your imagination to the audience applauding your efforts as you pose this incredible physique. And you can visualize yourself tasting and smelling one of your final precontest meals, your muscles straining to get through the skin. And this is the type of five-sense visualization that will push you to greatness in bodybuilding.

Candy Csencsits, twice Miss Olympia runner-up.

11

BODYBUILDING NUTRITION

Forty years of bodybuilding experience have taught us that nutrition is at least 50 percent of the battle in competitive bodybuilding. **Debbie Basile** (Lightweight American Champion) says, "It's axiomatic in bodybuilding that you are what you eat. Therefore, I am careful about the foods I consume during the off-season and more than careful about my diet prior to a competition. During a precontest cycle, 70–80 percent of my success is a result of my nutritional practices.

"Nonbodybuilders might consider a bodybuilder's diet unnecessarily bland, but all of us thrive on dietary self-discipline. I know precisely what foods and individual nutrients my body requires in order to continue making bodybuilding gains, and those are the only foods I eat. All serious women bodybuilders eat for function rather than for taste."

Nature hasn't made it easy for women to

reduce their body fat levels down to the minimum level required of a competitive bodybuilder. As a result, many women abuse their bodies with diets so low in calories as to be harmful to human health. It's not unusual for some women bodybuilders to consume as few as 500–700 calories per day prior to a competition.

Bodybuilders who adhere to excessively low-calorie diets when peaking for a competition pay a terrible price. Not only is an extremely low-calorie diet harmful to your health, but it also leads to binge eating. It's such an ordeal to get into shape that it's easy to overeat once the competition is over. This leads to a ballooning of an athlete's body weight, making it doubly difficult to reach contest shape for a succeeding competition.

The key to getting into contest shape safely and painlessly is keeping within five to seven pounds of competitive shape during the off-

167

season. And you must monitor your diet year-round in order to do this. But when you stay within striking distance of competitive condition, it's easy to get into shape. You probably won't need to go under 1,500 calories per day, and won't need to diet for more than six to eight weeks to reach a peak.

Rachel McLish (World Champion and twice Miss Olympia) understands this process better than most women bodybuilders: "I have never had to diet for more than six weeks or go under about 1,500 calories per day in my precontest diet because I stay in good shape year-round and use plenty of aerobics to help burn off excess body fat. And when I am able to consume plenty of food prior to a competition, I'm not only very muscular, but also am able to maintain more muscle mass than those women who diet on exceedingly low-calorie regimens."

DIETARY LEARNING

Perhaps you already know quite a bit about bodybuilding nutrition. Even if you do, there are books of nutrition information that you still need to assimilate in order to maximize your bodybuilding gains. You should read every diet article published in bodybuilding magazines, as well as the nutrition books that you find in health food stores.

One problem with nutrition study, however, is that there are a host of charlatans in the field. Everyone seems to have an ax to grind—primarily because they promote some "special" food product—and they disseminate considerable misinformation about nutrition. As a result, you must become a filter that can sort out and discard useless nutrition information.

You already have at your disposal the single best tool for evaluating nutrition data: the Weider Instinctive Training Principle. Using your instinctive training ability, you can give various nutritional techniques a try in your body lab and decide conclusively whether or not the new dietary process will aid your bodybuilding efforts.

Diet is just as important as training in the bodybuilding process, so you should system-

atically study nutrition texts and articles in an effort to learn everything you can about bodybuilding diet. As you grow in the sport, you will discover that all champion bodybuilders are walking encyclopedias of sports nutrition. And if you study bodybuilding nutrition in a consistent manner, you will soon equal the champs' knowledge of the subject.

NUTRITION NO-NOS

There are five nutritional practices that you should avoid if you wish to maintain a good rate of bodybuilding gains:

1. *Do not eat junk foods.* By junk foods we mean any food containing refined sugar, white flour, or any other highly processed food components. You should also avoid fried foods and other dishes containing excess fats.

2. *Do not consume excessive amounts of animal fats.* Try to eat low-fat meats such as fish, chicken, turkey, and veal. If you must eat beef or pork, choose the leanest cuts of meat and carefully cut away visible fat. Avoid full-fat milk and milk products and don't eat more than one or two egg yolks per day (egg whites are quite good for you, though). And while you should avoid animal fats, don't be afraid to consume vegetable fats in grains, seeds, and nuts. Vegetable fats do not harm your arterial system, and they are essential for the health of your body, particularly your nervous system.

3. *Avoid salting and/or otherwise seasoning your food.* The sodium in table salt and other foods (such as the artificial sweeteners in diet drinks) retains an enormous amount of water in your body. Body water retention can make you appear bloated and can lead to hypertension (high blood pressure).

4. *Don't drink excessive amounts of alcohol or highly sugared drinks.* In general, avoid drinking your calories. It's very easy to drink more than 1,000 calories of fruit juice, versus actually eating the fruit processed to yield juice.

5. *Don't eat after 6:00 P.M.* Eating late in the day will cause your body to store calories as

body fat much more easily than eating during the day. Only when attempting to gain weight should you eat late in the day.

DIETARY DOS

If you adhere to the following eight dietary rules, you will take a giant step toward maximizing your bodybuilding potential:

1. *Consume only small amounts of protein each time you eat.* Your digestive system can process only 20–25 grams of protein in each meal (the amount varies according to body size and relative digestive efficiency). Although vegetable protein sources can provide your body with some of the amino acids you require to build muscle, you will get the best assimilation of food protein into muscle tissue if you consume primarily animal-source proteins. The best sources of protein for bodybuilders are fish, poultry, low-fat meats, egg whites, nonfat milk products, and seed sprouts. Try to eat at least a little of one of these first-class protein foods at each meal.

2. *Eat plenty of fresh fruits and vegetables (approximately half of your total calories should come from fruits and vegetables).* Eat fruits and vegetables in as raw a state as possible. And if you do cook your vegetables, lightly steam them in order to retain maximum nutrients in the food. Don't throw all of your vitamins and minerals away with the cooking water.

3. *Consume at least one serving of high-fiber food per day.* Grain bran, salad greens, pears, and apples are high in roughage (fiber). Roughage keeps your digestive tract clean and in good working order, and it helps maintain good bowel habits.

4. *Drink at least eight glasses of fresh water per day.* If you live in an urban area, it's best to drink either bottled spring water or distilled water. Most municipal water contains enough chemicals to embalm a fair-sized cat.

5. *Eat a little vegetable fat each day from grains, seeds, and nuts.* The unsaturated fatty acids and lipotropics in vegetable oils actually help metabolize fat in your body. Saf-flower oil is a superior source of both unsaturated fatty acids and lipotropics. Try to use safflower oil and vinegar on your salads.

6. *Eat with as much variety as possible.* North Americans tend to eat the same 10–15 foods day in and day out. Since each food is deficient in at least one nutrient, it's counterproductive to eat only a limited spectrum of foods. It's much better to eat many different foods in an effort to allow the various nutrients in each food to complement nutrients in the others you consume.

7. *Eat small meals frequently throughout the day.* The nutrients in large meals are difficult to digest and assimilate, so bodybuilders have gotten away from eating the traditional two or three huge meals each day. Instead, they consume four to six smaller meals spaced out evenly during the day.

8. *Supplement your diet with vitamins and minerals as insurance against progress-stalling nutritional deficiencies.* At a minimum, take one or two multiple vitamin-mineral tablets, preferably with meals (you will get the best assimilation of vitamins and minerals if you consume them with other foods). Even better nutritional insurance would be one or two supplemental multipacks of vitamins, minerals, and trace elements each day. Weider Good Life Multipaks are one of the best, and they're available in all health food stores.

WEIGHT-GAIN DIET

There are literally millions of underweight women who would do almost anything to reach a more normal body weight. And there are thousands of women bodybuilders seeking to gain additional body mass. In both cases, added body fat is not acceptable; only an increase in overall muscle mass will result in the desired appearance improvement.

Heavy bodybuilding workouts stimulate your muscles to increase in mass and strength, but only if you also supply your body with sufficient amino acids from protein foods for muscle growth. And the best way to assure your body of receiving sufficient amino acids is to consume frequent, high-protein meals during the day.

We mentioned previously that your body can digest and make ready for assimilation into muscle tissue only 20–25 grams of protein in each meal. So if you eat only two meals per day, you have a maximum of 50 grams of protein in your system; and with three meals per day, you have no more than 75 grams of protein available for use in building larger muscles.

Given your limited ability to digest protein, the solution to pushing more amino acids into your bloodstream is eating more than three meals per day. And in actual practice serious women bodybuilders will consume four to six small high-protein meals each day when they are attempting to gain muscular body weight.

Following is a sample daily menu for gaining muscular body weight:

- **Meal #1** (8:00 A.M.)—cheese omelette, hamburger patty, piece of fruit, milk, supplements.
- **Meal #2** (10:30 A.M.)—tuna or meat sandwich, seeds or nuts, milk.
- **Meal #3** (1:00 P.M.)—broiled chicken breast, rice, salad (your choice of dressing), iced tea with fructose.
- **Meal #4** (3:30 P.M.)—protein drink (8-10 ounces of milk, tablespoon of milk and egg protein powder, banana or strawberries, all blended to a creamy consistency).
- **Meal #5:** (6:00 P.M.)—broiled steak, potato, vegetable, milk, supplements.
- **Meal #6** (8:30 P.M.)—boiled eggs, cold cuts, seeds or nuts, milk.

Since you are eating frequently, you won't consume very large portions of food at any meal. In essence, you will be snacking all day long, never allowing yourself to get hungry. And eating small meals like this will actually improve your digestive efficiency since larger meals tend to clog up your digestive tract.

One other way to improve digestive efficiency is to take digestive enzymes, which are available at all health food stores. Enzyme tablets definitely help you digest more food at each meal.

WEIGHT-LOSS DIET

In the past, a low-carbohydrate diet was widely used by men and women hoping to reduce body weight. While this diet does work, the side effects from it can range from uncomfortable to downright dangerous. A low-carb diet is harmful to your health, results in low energy levels and irritability, and often causes binge eating.

For the last several years competitive bodybuilders have almost universally used a low-calorie diet, which results in a safe and sane loss of excess body fat. By reducing the amount of fat in their diet, they automatically reduce the total number of calories they consume, which in turn results in a fatty body weight loss.

Again, fat is more than twice as rich a source of calories as either protein or carbohydrate (fat yields nine calories per gram, versus about four each for protein and carbohydrate). So when you replace fats in your diet with either protein or carbohydrate you inevitably eat fewer calories each day. And when you eat fewer calories you gradually lose body fat, particularly if you are also using up extra calories through weight training and aerobic exercise.

What foods are high in fats? The main culprits are animal-source foods such as full-fat milk and milk products, beef, pork, egg yolks, and the skin on poultry (although the meat itself is relatively low in fat). And what foods are lowest in fat content? The best weight-reduction foods are fish, skinless poultry, vegetables, fruits, and most grains and seeds.

Following is a sample low-fat/low-calorie daily diet that you can try out:

- *Breakfast*—egg whites, bran cereal with nonfat milk, piece of fruit, supplements, coffee or tea with fructose.
- *Lunch*—tuna salad made with water-packed tuna and low-fat salad dressing, slice of whole-grain bread (no butter), iced tea with fructose.
- *Dinner*—broiled chicken breast, rice, green salad with lemon juice and/or vinegar as a dressing, coffee or tea with fructose, supplements.

- *Snacks*—Popcorn (without salt or butter), cold chicken, nonfat yogurt, fresh fruit.

With a calorie-counter booklet in hand you can easily identify other low-fat/low-calorie foods and include them in your diet. And when you have worked out a week of meal plans you'll find that you experience very little hunger on a low-fat diet, while losing a safe one or two pounds of body fat each week.

PRECONTEST DIET

A precontest bodybuilding diet is very similar to the low-fat diet just described. The only difference is in the way the diet is applied and in the strict attention to controlling sodium intake.

If you have kept your body weight within five or six pounds of contest condition in the off-season, you should begin a precontest diet four to six weeks before you plan to step onstage in competitive condition. This will allow you plenty of time to take the weight off slowly and safely, without risking loss of precious muscle tissue. But if you have allowed your weight to balloon out of sight, you may have to diet for three months or more in order to even approach contest condition.

An effective bodybuilding diet is incremental. The first week you will cut back only a little on the number of calories that you have been consuming in the off-season. In most cases this involves merely cutting out any sweets or other junk foods that you might have allowed into your diet and perhaps eating 5 percent less fat each day.

With each succeeding week you should eat 200 or 300 fewer calories per day, until you are down to a minimum level of 1,200 (for smaller women) to 1,500 (for larger competitors) calories per day. And if you aren't getting cut up on this minimum-level caloric intake, it's better to increase your level of aerobic activity than to decrease the amount of food you're eating. Consuming less than 1,200–1,500 calories per day will be flirting with muscle mass loss, and no serious body-

builder can afford to lose some of the muscle she has worked so hard in the off-season to acquire.

When you're peaking for a major championship you have to watch your sodium intake like a hawk. Even tiny amounts of sodium will cause a major retention of body water. Obvious dietary sources of sodium are table salt (which is liberally added to virtually all processed foods) and artificial sweeteners (as in diet foods and diet drinks, which are sweetened with sodium saccharide). A less obvious culprit is celery, which is loaded with sodium.

Your best bet will be to obtain a book that lists the sodium content of all foods. One of the best books for this purpose is the *Nutrition Almanac* (McGraw-Hill, 1975). It's relatively inexpensive, and I'm sure you can purchase one at a health food store or general book store.

FOOD SUPPLEMENTS

Food supplements are concentrated vitamins, minerals, trace elements, proteins, and other whole foods in dried form. Virtually all serious bodybuilders use food supplements every day, and some rely quite heavily on dietary supplements.

As mentioned earlier, the first supplements you will probably take are multiple vitamin-mineral capsules or multipacks of vitamins, minerals, and trace elements. We recommend taking at least three to five tablets (or one or two multipacks) per day.

Later you will use a powdered protein supplement, especially when you've embarked on a weight-gaining program. Be sure your protein supplement is made primarily of milk- and/or egg-source protein concentrate. Milk and eggs are more efficiently converted into muscle tissue. You will find that soya-based protein is much less expensive than milk-and-egg protein powder, but you will also discover that you get less out of the vegetable-source protein powders.

Water-soluble vitamins and minerals (B-complex, C, potassium, calcium, and magnesium are most crucial) should be taken as individual supplements with at least one meal per day. In the case of B-complex and C you should think about taking each supplement two or three times per day if you wish to make truly outstanding bodybuilding gains.

After you've experimented with the foregoing vitamins and minerals—using the Weider Instinctive Training Principle to evaluate your results—you should consider adding other individual minerals and all oil-soluble vitamins to your supplementation program. However, you won't need to take oil-soluble vitamins (A, D, E, K, and P) more frequently than once per day. Oil-soluble vitamins are stored in your body and used up gradually throughout the day, in contrast to water-soluble vitamins, which are flushed out of your body immediately.

One final food supplement that all bodybuilders should consider is dessicated liver tablets. These tablets are whole liver that has been defatted, dried at a low temperature, then compressed into tablets. And dessicated liver has an almost miraculous effect on your energy levels throughout the day.

Two decades ago scientists conducted an experiment with lab rats who were fed three types of diets. Group One was fed a normal lab-rat diet for six weeks; Group Two was fed the lab-rat diet plus synthetic vitamins; and Group Three was fed the lab-fat diet plus all of the dessicated liver that the rats wanted to consume.

After six weeks on the various diets each group was placed in a drum of water from which they could not emerge. They were forced literally to swim or drown, a pure test of muscular endurance.

Group One rats swam an average of about 15 minutes before drowning; Group Two rats lasted only a little longer; but Group Three rats swam more than twice as long as either other group before drowning, and two rats were still swimming vigorously at the end of two hours when the scientists terminated the experiment. Had they not eaten dessicated liver, these two rats never would have survived.

You can also improve your workout energy levels by consuming dessicated liver. Take at least 10 tablets per day, either with meals or one hour prior to your workout. Some champion bodybuilders take 50 or more dessicated liver tablets per day, particularly when they are peaking for a competition.

ANIMAL versus VEGETABLE FATS

You definitely should avoid the saturated fats found in beef, pork, full-fat milk products, egg yolks, and other animal-source foods. Even though women suffer far less from heart and vascular disease then men, saturated fats have been implicated as a culprit in cardiovascular disease. You should also avoid eating coconut or hydrogenated vegetable oils (shortening), which are also high in saturated fats.

Most vegetable fats, however, are actually beneficial to your body, as long as you don't consume them to such an excess that your body weight increases. Vegetable fats are high in lipotropics, which promote heart and vascular health and actually assist in burning fat in your body. As a result, many bodybuilders will consciously include a tablespoon of safflower oil (high in lipos, particularly in lineolic acid) in their diets, usually as salad dressing. The safflower oil helps them lose excess body fat and reach competitive condition more easily.

PROTEIN

Protein foods are a bodybuilding staple because they provide the amino acids that form muscle tissue. There are 22 amino acids, eight of which are termed essential since they can't be manufactured within the human body. The eight essential amino acids must be present in sufficient quantities in the food you eat.

Animal proteins are the best sources of essential amino acids. The more essential amino acids in a food, the higher its Protein Efficiency Ration (PER), or the more easily and completely your body can use it for tissue maintenance and growth. Fish meal has the highest PER, followed by egg white and milk. Lesser but still high PERs can be found in whole fish, poultry, beef, and pork.

Vegetable proteins are usually quite low or totally deficient in one or more essential amino acids and as such are relatively poor sources of protein for most bodybuilders. Only seed sprouts and soybeans are reasonably good vegetarian sources of all essential amino acids.

By combining vegetable-source proteins with animal-source proteins, however, you can increase the PER of the vegetable proteins without denaturing the animal proteins. Following are three time-proven protein-food combinations.

- Rice + Beans + Milk (or milk products)
- Corn + Milk
- Rice + Beans + Meat (fish, poultry, beef, pork)

There is considerable debate in nutrition circles about how much protein is necessary in the average American diet as well as in an active athlete's diet. We personally believe that one-half to one gram of protein per pound of body weight is about right for an active bodybuilder, as long as the protein comes from first-class sources. The FDA, however, recommends less than one-half gram per pound of body weight each day, and many vegetarians eat as little as one-fourth gram per pound of body weight.

Ultimately, you'll need to use your nutritional instinct to determine how much protein you should be eating each day. Start with about one-half gram per pound of body weight each day, then gradually work your protein consumption up toward the one-gram-per-day figure. Along the way, note how each amount of protein affects your ability to make good gains from your bodybuilding training.

One thing is clear: too much protein (probably much more than one gram per pound of body weight each day) can be harmful to your kidneys, particularly if you don't also consume plenty of fresh water. So, if you are consuming close to one gram per pound per day, be sure to drink extra water (at least a couple of glasses above your normal level of consumption) each day.

Corrine Machado-Ching, Ms. Western America.

12
FINE TUNING

Putting everything together to reach peak competitive shape is an art form. Like a symphony conductor who must blend the sounds of scores of musical instruments to yield the sweet music of a Beethoven symphony, you must orchestrate your bodybuilding training, aerobic workouts, diet, mental preparations, tanning efforts, and posing practice to result in optimum condition and general preparedness for competition.

It's unlikely that you will reach an optimum peak the first time you prepare for a bodybuilding championship. You'll probably have to make several peaking attempts, taking good mental, written, and photographic notes of how your body reacts to each external stimulus. Most particularly, you must develop a series of checkpoints set at one-week intervals for the final six to eight weeks before a competition and one-day intervals the last week before you compete. When you

know what type of shape you have to be in at each checkpoint you can gauge whether or not you need to speed up or slow down the peaking process. Timing like this is everything in competitive bodybuilding.

In this chapter we will discuss the following topics related to competitive bodybuilding: cycle training; quality training; peak contraction; continuous tension; isotension; how a competition is conducted; posing; grooming, tanning, and suit choice; and birth control and menstruation. Assimilation of this new information will give you the best possible chance of peaking successfully and on schedule for your next competition.

CYCLE TRAINING

"No bodybuilder can hope to maintain peak physical condition indefinitely," reveals **Candy Csencsits** (runner-up, Miss Olympia).

175

Kike Elomaa and Candy Csencsits before the 1982 Miss Olympia.

"Both your mind and body need a rest from the intense preparations inherent in the peaking process."

Candy hits at the heart of the Weider Cycle Training Principle in which seasons of heavy, lesser-intensity training and relaxed diet are alternated with cycles of high-intensity training and strict diet. If you stayed in a precontest training and dietary mode all year, you would quickly burn out. You would also fail to build as much muscle as you would if you periodically underwent an off-season phase in which you trained with very heavy weights on primarily basic exercises.

You will have two main objectives during an off-season cycle: gradually add muscle mass to your physique and specifically improve your worst one or two muscle groups. The process used to accomplish these two tasks involves the following factors:

1. Either do four workouts per week (if you have less than one year of training experience) or maintain a four-day training cycle, three training days followed by one day of rest.

2. Each major muscle group is trained two (or slightly more than two) times per week. Calves can be worked three or four times a week and abdominals on a daily basis.

3. No more than 10–12 total sets are performed for each major/complex muscle group (thighs, back, chest and shoulders) and no more than six to eight total sets for other body parts.

4. Take up to two minutes of rest between sets for large body parts and no more than one minute of rest between sets for smaller muscle groups.

5. Use primarily basic exercises for low reps (from three to six) in each set.

6. Maintain strict form while taking each post-warm-up set at least to the point of momentary muscular failure. Up to half of all sets can be extended past the point of failure by using the Weider Cheating, Forced Reps, and Descending Sets Training Principles.

7. Lagging muscle groups should be attacked with maximum training intensity early in each workout when you have optimum mental and physical energies available to blast them into submission. This is use of the Weider Muscle Priority Training Principle.

8. Do no more than three 30- to 45-minute aerobic training sessions per week.

9. Take in up to 5 percent more than your caloric maintenance level until you are five or six pounds over your competitive weight; thereafter, you should stay at your maintenance level.

10. Get plenty of sleep and rest.

During a precontest (or peaking) cycle your primary objective will be to strip away all possible body fat in order to reveal the hard-earned new muscle mass lying under this extra padding. You will not be able to improve the mass and contour of a lagging muscle group during a peaking cycle. The process used to reach a competitive peak encompasses the following factors.

1. Do six workouts per week, training each major muscle group either two or three times a week. Calves can still be trained three to four days per week, while abdominals should be worked virtually every day.

2. Up to 18–20 total sets can be performed for each major muscle group for a short period of time. Do up to 10–12 total sets for smaller body parts.

3. Slash rest intervals between sets to less than one minute for larger body parts and to as little as 30 seconds for smaller muscle groups.

4. Continue to use one or two basic exercises for each body part, but increase the number of isolation movements you do in your workouts. You should particularly turn to cable and machine isolation movements in an effort to bring out maximum muscle density.

5. Use ultrastrict form, plus the Weider Slow, Continuous Tension; Peak Contraction; and Isotension Training Principles to bring out peak intensity in your workouts.

6. Train your largest muscle groups early in each workout, saving the smaller body parts for later when you wouldn't have the energy to bomb your thighs, back, or chest.

7. Do up to one or two hours of steady-state aerobic training per day, the amount varying according to your energy levels and how close you are to being on schedule in your peaking cycle.

8. For the most advanced bodybuilders, more than one training session (particularly when the second workout consists primarily of aerobics) per day is acceptable.

9. Reduce your caloric intake by 5–10 percent, the degree of reduction depending on how much more fat you need to lose and how much time you have in which to lose it.

10. Begin tanning at least four to six weeks before competing in order to come into the show with a deep, even tan. Of course, this does not apply to dark-skinned bodybuilders.

11. Practice posing every day, preferably for at least one hour at a time. Be sure to practice each of the three main rounds of posing (which will be explained later in this chapter).

Transition Periods

It's hard on your body when you move abruptly from one cycle to another, so you should always include a transition cycle of one or two weeks between off-season and pre-contest cycles. During a transition phase you should gradually move from one type of training and diet to the next. And after a competition you should take one or two weeks to gradually wind down your training before you consider taking a short layoff and then building back up to off-season-level training intensity and dietary laxity.

Other Considerations

It takes a great deal of self-discipline and

self-sacrifice to peak out optimally on the day of a major competition, and the best bodybuilders are almost always the ones who have first paid their dues with several years of gym training and then put out maximum effort in their peaking cycle. There's really no other way to do it.

You will also find it advantageous to use the visualization technique during your peaking cycle. With this technique you spend 15–30 minutes each night just before you go to bed "daydreaming" about the physique you wish to display onstage at your next competition. Nighttime is best for visualization practice because you will have the fewest distractions and the best concentration ability then.

Start the visualization process by first lying in a comfortable position and systematically relaxing your entire body. After five or ten minutes you should be totally relaxed, at which point you can begin to imagine vividly how your body will appear onstage. Make this visualized image as realistic as possible—imagining even the sound of an enthusiastic bodybuilding crowd applauding your efforts and the scent of the oil on your body—and you will have programmed your powerful subconscious mind to assist your weaker conscious mind in accomplishing each task necessary to peak optimally and on the exact day of your competition.

QUALITY TRAINING

Most champion bodybuilders use the Weider Quality Training Principle during the weeks leading up to a major championship because quality training combines well with a calorie-restricted diet and such other training intensification techniques as peak contraction, continuous tension, and isotension to bring out a maximum of muscular striations. Quality training consists of progressively reducing the length of rest intervals between sets to a minimum level of about 30 seconds.

You should remember from the discussion in Chapter 2 that there are basically three ways in which you can increase the amount of intensity you place on a working muscle group:

1. Use a heavier weight in an exercise.
2. Use the same amount of weight, but progressively increase the number of repetitions that you do with it.
3. Do the same number of sets and reps with a consistent weight in an exercise, but progressively decrease the length of rest intervals between sets.

With quality training you will be using primarily the third method of intensity progression. However, you will find it very difficult to reduce your rest intervals and still use the same exercise weights in your workouts, particularly in light of the fact that precontest dieting will reduce the usual amount of energy that you have available for your workouts.

"You have to expect your training weights to fall somewhat when you are quality training," explains **Lori Bowen** (American and USA Champion). "However, the trick to using the Weider Quality Training Principle effectively is to always use maximum poundages, even though they may be relatively lighter than what you handle in off-season training. Don't use quality training as an excuse to slack off on your intensity because that would be counterproductive when you're peaking out. Push hard all of the time, and you'll come out with the best quality of muscularity."

It would be difficult for us to tell you how much you will lose from each exercise's training poundages for every week that you are quality training, since every body reacts somewhat differently. But if you have lost more than 20–25 percent from one or more exercises, you are undoubtedly resting too little between sets and should increase your rest intervals about five or more seconds between sets.

PEAK CONTRACTION

Physiologists have determined that each individual muscle cell in one of the many muscle fibers that make up each skeletal muscle, when it is put under a load, con-

Lori Bowen.

Within a muscle fiber in your body the total number of muscle cells fired off (contracted) depends on two factors—how short the muscle fiber must become and how heavy a load has been placed on the muscle. And when you have your biceps muscles fully flexed (or fully shortened) and also under a heavy load you will have the maximum number of individual muscle cells fired off. It just makes good sense, then, that you could most powerfully stress and optimally stimulate muscle growth in a particular muscle if you placed a maximum load on it when it is in its fully contracted position.

The basis of the Weider Peak Contraction Training Principle is to place a very heavy load on the muscles when they are completely contracted. Unfortunately, however, many exercises do not allow a peak contraction effect. For example, there is absolutely no resistance on your biceps in the finish position of a Barbell Curl movement. In point of fact, the weight in that position is supported primarily by the deltoid and upper back muscles.

You can put a peak contraction effect on your biceps either by doing Machine Curls or by performing Barbell Concentration Curls with a narrow undergrip on the bar and your torso held parallel to the floor. In this position you must actively contract your biceps muscles in order to keep your arms fully bent. Other good peak contraction exercises are those done on most machines, plus Barbell Bent Rows, Upright Rows, Dumbbell Concentration Curls, One-Leg Calf Raises, and various types of Lateral Raises with both a barbell and two dumbbells.

CONTINUOUS TENSION

The Weider Slow, Continuous Tension Training Principle combines well with the Weider Peak Contraction Training Principle to etch cuts deeply into each muscle mass. And continuous tension is the technique that you should use in order to *feel* a muscle working along its full range of contraction and extension.

Many bodybuilders make the mistake of

tracts (shortens) either completely or it doesn't contract at all. This is called the "all or nothing" model of muscle contraction, and it has a direct bearing on use of the Weider Peak Contraction Training Principle.

To illustrate how the "all or nothing" model works, let's visualize a muscle fiber as one long rope of wool socks tied together, the socks representing individual muscle cells, which in fact are similarly strung end to end. If you selectively shrunk one sock—the same as one muscle cell would contract—the full rope of socks would be somewhat shorter as a result. You could further shorten the rope by shrinking two, three, or more socks.

moving a weight too quickly as they perform an exercise. As a result, momentum robs them of resistance on the working muscles along part of an exercise's range of motion, depriving them of much of the stimulation the muscles should have received.

By moving the weight slowly and over an exaggerated range of motion you can put a lot more stress on a muscle. And this is one tenet of the Weider Slow, Continuous Tension Training Principle. A second is to build maximum tension into the working muscle, first by consciously tensing it to the limit and second by also contracting the antagonistic muscle(s). So when you are doing Dumbbell Concentration Curls, you will have both your biceps and triceps tensed, and you will move the weight slowly over the exercise's complete range of motion.

Continuous tension sets tend to make your muscles cry for mercy as fatigue toxins rapidly build up in them. They also make it difficult to use a very heavy weight, particularly because you add resistance to one muscle by contracting the antagonistic muscle. But a good woman bodybuilder can make a 20-pound dumbbell feel like it weighs 40 when she uses the Weider Slow, Continuous Tension Training Principle with her Dumbbell Concentration Curls. And in the process, she'll build some incredible muscle density into her biceps.

ISOTENSION CONTRACTION

One of the newest advances in bodybuilding training resulting in improved contest muscularity is the Weider Isotension Contraction Training Principle. Many years ago bodybuilders discovered that there was a direct relationship between the amount of posing practice they put in and their ultimate degree of competition muscularity. It was clear that the more posing they did, the more muscular they became, so we reasoned that hard muscle tensing would improve muscular definition.

There are two reasons that hard muscle flexes improve muscularity. First, consistent flexing of a muscle gives you better control over the muscle, which in turn allows you to display greater muscularity onstage. Secondly, the actual hard tensing is similar enough to the intense muscle contractions of heavy bodybuilding training to improve. muscle density.

As codified by Joe Weider, the Weider Isotension Contraction Training Principle consists of many "repetition" flexes of each major muscle group, each flex lasting 8–10 seconds. Additionally, each muscle is flexed in a variety of positions for several reps in each position. At least 20 flexes, and up to a maximum of 30, are performed between the various positions for each muscle group.

Let's use the biceps muscles as an example of the Weider Isotension Principle in action. With both arms up in a double biceps pose, flex your biceps as hard as you can for 10 seconds. Rest for 10–15 seconds and flex them again in the same position. Repeat this double biceps flexing 10 times. Next, place your hands together in front of your hips as if doing a most-muscular pose, then bring them up to your chest, where you can flex your biceps with great intensity. Do 10 rep flexes in this position, resting for 10–15 seconds between each flex. Finally, place your hands behind your head as for a front abdominal pose and flex your biceps in this position for 10 more reps. This should leave your biceps throbbing and pumped to the limit.

Some bodybuilders use the isotension technique between sets for a particular muscle group, but we prefer to schedule isotension workouts separate from bodybuilding training sessions. So, if you work out in the gym during the morning, you can come back in the afternoon or evening and do a good isotension session. And be sure that you break slowly into a full isotension workout, starting with only 8–10 flexes for each muscle group.

You can do isotension year-round, but it's best used during the last four to six weeks prior to a show when you're trying to really harden up. During the last two or three weeks before a competition you can do isotension for each body part virtually every day, or at least two out of every three days.

And prior to that you can perform an isotension workout every other day. This frequency of isotension workouts will bring out the finest details of muscularity faster than you could hope to imagine!

BODYBUILDING COMPETITION

You can learn an incredible amount about actually competing merely by attending a bodybuilding competition, so it's essential that you attend several competitions before actually jumping into the fray yourself. It would be foolhardy to enter your first bodybuilding show totally cold, even though you'll see many women in competition with zero knowledge of how to conduct themselves.

First, you'll need to determine which competitions are coming up in your area, so you can obtain tickets well enough in advance to ensure good seating at both the prejudging and evening shows. Upcoming competitions are advertised in bodybuilding coming-events columns in *Flex* and other bodybuilding magazines, as well as via handbills and posters on the bulletin boards of gyms and spas in the immediate area of the show. An address or phone number for ticket information will appear on the poster or in the ad.

Be sure to obtain tickets for the prejudging as well as the evening show because the prejudging is where all of the real action at a bodybuilding competition takes place. Even if you must sit somewhat off to the side, find a seat as close to the stage as possible for the prejudging. For a good appreciation of how this crucial facet of the competition is conducted you must sit close enough to the stage and judging panel to hear the judges' instructions to the athletes.

AFWB/IFBB rules provide for a panel of seven judges, each of whom is certified to judge a particular level of competition (regional, national, etc.). Although you'll occasionally hear that judges are biased or incompetent, it is a very rare occurrence to encounter a poor bodybuilding judge. However, you must understand that judging is in the end a subjective procedure, even though

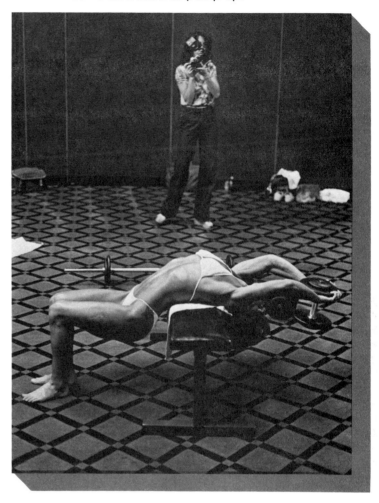

Backstage at the 1981 American Championship, a woman bodybuilder does some extensions to pump up.

it is governed by a firm set of rules and standards, so there are minor variations in placings from one show to the next.

There are three main rounds of judging, and in each round every judge ranks the contestants, making sure that he or she awards no tied placings. All of the judges' scores are entered opposite the name of each contestant on a scoring sheet. The high and low scores for each contestant are dropped, and the remaining five scores in each round are totaled for a round score. The contestant with the lowest score is the round winner. Finally, all three round scores are added up to determine prejudging placings, which can be altered slightly at the evening posedown.

It's important to note that each of the three main rounds of posing reveal different

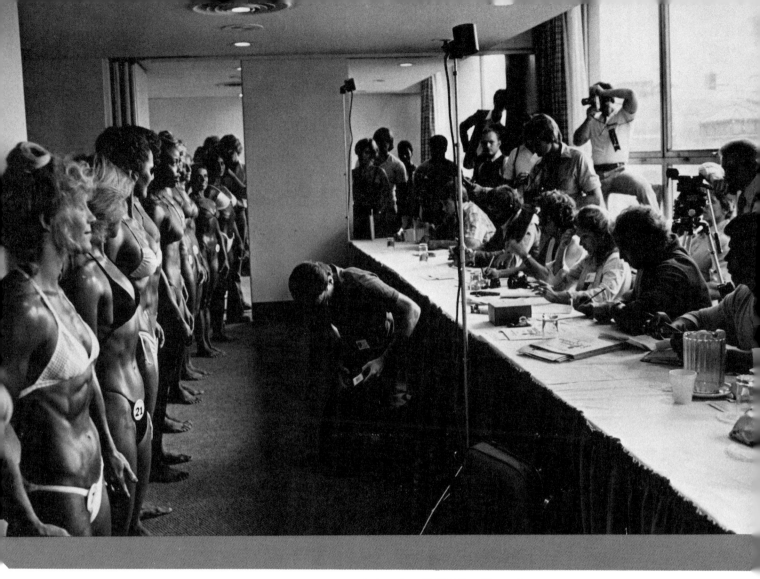

Prejudging line-up during the 1980 Miss Olympia.

physical qualities, and it's the aggregate of scores that reveals the champion of a particular competition. You will often see a woman who is very good at one or perhaps two rounds, but who falls down so badly in others that her total score places her out of the top position. And this is how it should be, for overall excellence is always rewarded over partial excellence in the world of sport.

The first round of posing consists of five standardized compulsory poses that reveal each competitor's physique under rigidly equal conditions. At the time of writing this book the Round I poses were front double biceps, side chest, back double biceps, side triceps, and front abdominal/thigh.

After each contestant has performed her Round I poses individually, the judges will call all bodybuilders onstage for a line-up from which they will select groups of two, three, and occasionally more for direct comparisons. These comparisons tend to be time-consuming, but they are essential because it's impossible for a judge to rank every woman accurately without comparing her with those contestants near her ultimate placing. Incidentally, the more you watch bodybuilding competitions, the more easily you will be able to tell who is winning merely by observing which bodybuilders are being compared by the judges.

Round II of the IFBB judging system consists of four semirelaxed stances performed with feet close together and arms down at the sides. You will begin the series facing the judges. Then you will turn your left side toward the panel, your back, your right side, and again your front. To individuals unfamil-

Backstage at the 1980 Miss Olympia, contestants assist each other in applying body oils.

iar with bodybuilding this round of posing probably reveals very little. However, an experienced judge can gain an appreciation for general body symmetry (the shape of various muscles and parts of the body), the proportional balance among major muscle groups, and general muscle tone from the Round II stances.

As in Round I, comparisons are made at the conclusion of Round II. In Round III, however, no comparisons are made, since everyone does a different routine. In both Round I and Round II the judges will refrain from marking their score sheets until they have compared all contestants.

Round III is the free-posing round in which each bodybuilder does a uniquely individual, free-flowing posing routine to her own choice of music (you will be required to provide a cassette recording of your musical selection). During your free-posing routine you will have an opportunity to display your strong points and camouflage your weak areas to your heart's content, something you

Comparison judging at the 1982 Miss Olympia. In the front line, left to right, are Lynn Conkwright, Carla Dunlap, Laura Combes, and Candy Csencsits.

The Big Show: the audience sees the pageantry of the contestants lined up in the background and a guest poser in the foreground at the 1981 American Championships.

simply can't do in the first two rounds of judging.

The free-posing round is the most visually appealing of the three judging rounds, as you witness each woman calling on all of her choreography, dance, and gymnastics skill to display her physique to maximum advantage. And you should pay special attention to the unique transitional movements each woman uses to shift from one pose to another; you'll soon need to use similar transitions in your own free-posing routine.

At the end of three rounds the top five women are moved into a special posedown round in which they can earn valuable addi-

tional points. This posedown is usually conducted at the evening show, and it's very exciting to watch each woman attempt to muscle her way to the top against the other ranking competitors.

Finally, a winner is chosen by combining Round I, Round II, Round III, and posedown points, and she is awarded the winner's trophy. Take a good look at how excited she is because you'll be up there one day yourself if you have the self-discipline and ability to learn from your mistakes. After months and years of hard training and self-sacrifice it feels absolutely incredible to be up there accepting a trophy for your efforts.

Most competitions these days feature a champion bodybuilder or two in a guest-posing exhibition. Often Rachel McLish, Carla Dunlap, Shelley Gruwell, or some other woman bodybuilder will guest-pose, and you should observe her carefully. Guest posers are seldom in top shape because it's so difficult to peak out more than two or three times per year, but even in 90 percent condition they'll show you what you need to shoot for if your goal is to win a World Championship or Miss Olympia title. And these stars will invariably be among the best posers you will have ever seen.

What the Judges Look for

The most important physical quality that judges assess is the relative balance among your various body parts. If you are well developed except for having skinny calves, you won't score as highly in a competition as a woman who has even, harmonious body proportions.

As long as you have a minimum degree of muscle mass, the next most important quality for a woman bodybuilder is muscularity, or the absence of fat over the body that reveals hard-earned muscles beneath the skin. Muscle mass itself is a good quality to have, but it's much less important than proportional balance and good muscle tone/muscularity.

A third important quality is symmetry, or the overall shape of your physique and each muscle group that makes it up. To have good symmetry it helps to have relatively broad shoulders and a narrow waist (narrow hips, however, seem to be a drawback at the present time). You should also have relatively small joints surrounded by large muscle volumes. And it is advantageous to have long-appearing muscles, although this is a genetically determined quality that is almost impossible to improve through training.

Posing ability is also important, particularly in the third round of judging. If you can't display your body effectively, you won't rack up as many points as a woman with lesser development and greater posing abil-

ity. And having a flair for posing will really put an audience on your side at a show, which at least subconsciously affects the score that each judge awards you.

Finally, it helps to be well-groomed, have a good choice of posing attire, and have superior skin tone (darkly tanned, smooth, blemish-free skin).

CARLA DUNLAP ON POSING

Carla Dunlap (Miss Olympia, Pro World Champion, Caesar's Palace Pro Invitational Champion) is considered by many aficionados of the sport to be the master poser of women's bodybuilding. In a recent *Muscle & Fitness* magazine article she offered advice on posing to women bodybuilders: "The skill with which you pose at a competition can make the difference between winning and losing. It takes plenty of careful thought and practice to develop artistic posing ability.

"I firmly believe in practicing all three of the AFWB/IFBB posing rounds. When I first started competing I didn't practice the symmetry round, Round II. But when you understand that you receive one-third of your total score in that round it doesn't make much sense not to practice it. The situation is much like in ballet—you can just stand there, or you can stand there with presence.

"In bodybuilding you have to look good during the entire symmetry round because you are constantly on display. Actually, I feel that a person should practice standing with perfect posture and alignment even if she doesn't intend to compete. I've seen many people walk with one shoulder higher than the other, or with their spine tilted to one side. They will swear up and down that they are in perfect alignment, but to anyone observing them it's obvious that they aren't. Poor body alignment throws your proportions off.

"I have a few tricks that I use in Round II. For example, I have a small waist in comparison to some women bodybuilders, but it's not as small as it should be because I also have narrow hips. So I pull my rib cage up and slightly arch my back while standing

Carla Dunlap, the master poser of women's bodybuilding.

facing the judges; this gives the impression that my hips are just a little wider than they actually are. I don't have this problem from the back since the sweep of my lats is relatively good. For side views I ever-so-slightly pull my shoulders back and push my hips forward so it pulls my oblique muscles into long strands rather than leaving them bunched up.

"It's important to maintain good body carriage when standing in a lineup during comparisons," Ms. Dunlap continued. "If I am on a judging panel—and I think that every competitor should judge from time to time, just to get a judge's perspective in bodybuilding competition—my eyes will occasionally stray back to someone who may not be in the group under comparison. They certainly don't have to be smiling all of the time, but to gain my approval they have to have a confident, 'onstage' look. If you let deportment slip for a moment, it's difficult to get the approval of a judge."

Body Attitude

Carla continues: "You should smile and look confident onstage in every round of judging. There is no question that your body alignment and body language in general can project your emotions at the time—confidence, aggressiveness, and so forth. In ballet they call this 'body attitude.'

"Much of body attitude is mental. When I was competing in synchronized swimming we were told that once we stepped on deck we stepped out of whatever suit we were wearing and stepped into a competitive mode. In other words, we changed our attitude from whatever it was to a winning attitude. When we got out of the pool after a routine we might have been dying from exhaustion, but we couldn't show it until the scores had been posted. Out of the judges' eyes we could huff and puff, but when we were in front of them we had to make it look effortless.

"In bodybuilding you can project a winning attitude by mentally preparing yourself to compete and by being in the best possible

New Jersey, where I train, I'm surprised at how few people can do the compulsory poses in a manner that complements their body lines. There are certain stances and body positions that you should avoid, and there are little twists of the torso and other changes of body position that make each pose a bit more aesthetic and effective.

"Every bodybuilder adapts a compulsory pose to fit his or her own physique. You could cut out 10 photos of various women performing a front double-biceps pose, place them side by side, and you would immediately notice that none of them look alike. So you have to search for what looks best for you. For example, if you have good frontal thigh cuts, it doesn't make much sense to extend your leg to the side in a front double-biceps pose. You'd see far less thigh development with your leg out to the side than if you brought it around to the front.

"Many mistakes are made when doing the second women's compulsory pose, the side-chest stance. You must be particularly careful of how you place your feet and legs in this pose. The worst mistake in side shots—particularly in the side-chest pose—is dropping your chin. And many bodybuilders mistakenly crunch their shoulders forward. You have to be aware of these little details in order to assume a pose with maximum effectiveness.

"The two mandatory side poses have different leg positions. If your legs are well-developed, this shouldn't make a difference to you. I think it's fairer to have the variety, because you must have better leg development to do both types of leg stances. Incidentally, many bodybuilders are so busy worrying about their chest, shoulder, and arm muscles that they forget to tense their legs. You have to keep it all going at once, or the pose won't look as good as it should.

"Moving to the back double-biceps shot, you should be sure to keep your back open and your shoulder blades spread. Many bodybuilders crunch their shoulder blades together, which destroys any lat sweep, which in turn makes the pose appear odd. This is the only mandatory pose in which

condition. No doubt you have seen badly outclassed competitors onstage, and you've noticed their confidence quickly draining away as they become aware that they aren't in contention for the title. If you're perfectly prepared—both mentally and physically—for a competition, your attitude will be as good as it can be."

Compulsory Posing

Carla feels that it's vitally important to practice the mandatory poses of Round I because they also count toward a third of your score. She says, "When I work with many of the men and women at John and Shirley Kemper's Diamond Gym in Mapleton, you can display full calf development, so be sure to extend your leg to the rear—rather than to the side—and fully flex your calf. If you have good hamstring development, you should flex your rear thigh muscles.

"In the back double-biceps shot, as well as in other poses, you should not make the mistake of standing erect with your legs held straight. You should flex your knees slightly to add flow to your body line. A couple of other back double-biceps tricks are tensing your abdominals to help you fully contract your lower back muscles and turning your head to one side to bring out your trapezius development.

"I feel that the side triceps pose is another stance in which people either forget to tense their legs or tend to tense them incorrectly. You must extend the leg nearest the judges to the rear in this pose, but that doesn't mean that you have to keep the leg straight. If your leg is extended to the rear and slightly bent, you can learn how to flex your tush and leg biceps more, which brings out the muscularity on the side of your thigh.

"In both side poses you can bring out your calf a little better if you learn to pull your knee toward, and perhaps across, the midline of your body. You also need to do plenty of Seated Calf Raises in your leg workouts, since this movement etches good muscularity into the sides of your calves. Without good side-calf cuts it's difficult to hit any type of side shot with maximum effectiveness.

"The final mandatory pose is a thigh and abdominal shot performed with the hands held behind the head and neck. This is a shot in which many bodybuilders attempt to flex too hard. If you have good, sharp abdominals, you don't need to flex them really hard to display the deep cuts. I also don't believe in blowing out my air as I do an abdominal shot; I do it with strict muscle control instead. You don't necessarily have to expel your breath to contract your abdominal muscles.

"If you tend to have blocky body lines, you should drop one hip to the rear to reveal a better body line. Your legs should be held

with one foot forward, and your thighs should be tensed to reveal the maximum degree of quadriceps muscularity. A lot of bodybuilders forget that they can flex their biceps in this pose, perhaps by placing their hands behind their head with their fists closed. And you should remember to flex your arms hard without closing your elbows or dropping your hands to your chest."

Free Posing

Carla Dunlap also feels that the free-posing round is a chance to really strut her stuff: "You've already shown your physique technically in the first two rounds. The free-posing round is a showcase for your physique in an artistic sense, a time to show your personality, your ability to move your body aesthetically, and possibly to touch on the little details of your physique that haven't been addressed in the first two rounds. In Rounds I and II you're constricted, controlled, limited to a certain set pattern. In the free-posing round you suddenly get to break loose from these bonds and be yourself, totally free to move as you like.

"Music is far more important in the free-posing round than many bodybuilders think. I believe that women have grasped this far more easily and quickly than men. In every sense music should be used to emphasize movement and vice versa. Many bodybuilders choose music simply because it's required in the free-posing round, rather than picking a particular musical selection to enhance their presentation.

"Good posing is not a matter of having a natural talent for sensing the rhythm of a piece of music; it's a matter of knowing what music is all about. In the film *Flashdance*, Jennifer Beals makes a comment, 'Can't you see the music?' The comment goes right over her boyfriend's head. That's the way it is with most people—they hear a piece of music and they remember only the melody. What they don't hear and remember are the rhythm, subrhythm, and message of the song.

"You are not restricted to the melody and rhythm of a piece when you dance or pose to

The soaring joy in these photos typify Carla's ability to "see the music."

it. The person who has true command of music can jump back and forth between any accent, any melody, and any rhythm in music, and that is the highest level of musical mastery. A person might be singing, and you mime what he sings, then a bit later drop back and work with the melody or rhythm of the piece. The rhythm is always there, while the melody changes. And you should always make use of any accents in the music.

"Many women bodybuilders complain that competitors with a dance background have a big advantage in the free-posing round. That's like my complaining about a woman who has fantastic natural leg development. Do I complain? No, I get into the gym and do something about improving my own legs. If a bodybuilder is intelligent, she will look at other women and see what they do effectively, then adapt it for her own use. And if you don't have a dance background, go out and take some classes instead of moaning about it.

"It's sometimes difficult to evaluate how a particular pose or transition suits your physique and personality. I personally listen to almost anyone who has something to say about how I come across onstage. But I don't think you can get very good criticism from your friends, since you often can't do anything wrong in their eyes.

"It's difficult to define qualified criticism. If I'm told the same thing often enough, I get the message that it's something I should work on. In my own case qualified criticism is more by consensus than anything else.

"Let's say that you are preparing to compete for the first time, and you are working on your first free-posing routine. I think that at first it will imitate the posing routine of someone else whom you have seen compete. Great painters were first apprenticed to a great living artist, and everything they did at first was derivative of their master's work. But, as a painter matures, he begins to discover his own elements of style and his own artistic ability surfaces. It's something that must evolve and grow, the same concept as in bodybuilding posing.

"Balance and control come with movement experience. If someone who doesn't have good motor ability attempts to pose slowly and gracefully, it doesn't come off well. She probably wouldn't look graceful and controlled if she took classes from George Balanchine. But if someone has good motor control and lacks the muscle mass to do big, powerful poses, she should stay with graceful and artistic poses.

"Ultimately, you must develop a rapport with your audience and the judges. This shouldn't be to the point where you are doing cheesecake, but you should extend yourself to your viewers. The worst thing onstage is to see a bodybuilder who poses well but who remains in her own little bubble and doesn't share her routine with the audience. You have to open up and pull the people in to you."

Carla Dunlap concluded by noting, "Posing should come from the heart. Your posing should ultimately be you, not someone else. We who have been in the forefront of bodybuilding as it developed have had a better shot at being ourselves, while women who have recently surfaced in the sport are in a position where they may have to imitate poses to some extent.

"It's not easy to develop an effective onstage presentation, but when you get it right, you can really enjoy it. You can see the magic. You feel good about posing, and you let that excitement show through to your audience. You become a master sculptor who can get inside her sculpture and bring it to life for an audience. It's difficult to beat the feeling that comes when your audience applauds your efforts.. It's an unforgettable sensation!"

PERSONAL APPEARANCE

There are three factors of personal appearance—grooming, skin tone, and suit choice—that can have a bearing on how well you perform in a bodybuilding competition.

Your personal grooming should be fastidious and complementary to your facial features and coloring. Since the lighting onstage at a bodybuilding competition is relatively harsh, you'll need to wear somewhat heavier makeup than you would in normal surroundings. We suggest that you take a makeup kit with you to your first show and apply it according to how you see more experienced women doing their own makeup.

It's best for your hairstyle to be either short or pinned up, because it has to be off your shoulders where long hair could obscure your hard-earned muscularity. If you don't already have such a hairstyle, it would be a good idea to see a good hairstylist and have him or her design one appropriate for your general appearance.

Wearing jewelry onstage is very poor form, primarily because it is distracting. More than a ring and a thin neck chain would be pushing it. And at the evening show you can wear a flower, feathers, or whatever turns you on in your hair.

Light-skinned women will need to obtain an even, dark tan. The best tan is a natural one acquired through six or more weeks of sunbathing. Be sure to start out with only 10–15 minutes on each side, then gradually build up exposure time, turning your body frequently and lying at different angles in order to make sure the tan is even. You must avoid sunburn at all costs during the last week before your show, because your damaged skin will attract water as part of the healing process. Excess water in your skin will blur out muscular definition.

Of course, it's difficult to get a natural tan during the winter or in northern climes. The next best tan is obtained in a sunbed or sunbooth, although continued exposure to artificial light—as well as natural sunlight—can damage and age your skin.

A poor third place for skin color is a make-up or tanning cream. Creams normally leave you with an orange appearance to your skin, and many makeups rub right off or smear when you apply oil. The best chemical tans we have seen begin with a base of Dyoderm (available at drugstores), over which a powder makeup (Indian Earth and Beverly Hills Dirt are both popular and available at cosmetic counters) rubbed on over the Dyoderm.

Naturally, dark-skinned bodybuilders need not worry about getting a tan, but all body-builders must oil their skin prior to appearing onstage. Proper body oiling enhances the highlights on your muscles and gives your body a nice three-dimensional appearance.

Be sure that you use a vegetable oil (avocado, almond, olive, etc.) rather than a petroleum-based oil; vegetable oils sink into the skin and emerge slowly to give a glow to your skin, while petroleum oils lie on your skin like a coating of plastic freezer wrap.

Apply oil evenly to your body, rubbing it in hard. This way the oil will be in your pores and will emerge slowly as you warm up backstage and begin to perspire a little. And keep in mind that you may need to apply more oil periodically or even out your oil as prejudging continues.

Your suit choice boils down to three things: you must wear a bikini; it should be of a solid color, without reflective threads or other adornments; and the color should complement your general coloring. Other than adhering to these three factors, just be sure that the suit fits you well. And when you find one that fits, buy at least two; you'll find it comforting to have a spare posing costume to change into after one has been oil-spotted or otherwise soiled at a prejudging. You will find a handy chart of posing suit color choices in Figure 12–1.

	Lightly Tanned	Darkly Tanned	Brown	Black
RED HAIR	Medium Blue, Medium to Dark Green	Gold, Yellow		
BLOND HAIR	Red, Royal Blue, Black	Burgundy, Red, Medium Blue, Orange		
BROWN HAIR	Black, Navy Blue	Burgundy, Brown, Purple, Teal	Black, Yellow, Chocolate Brown	
BLACK HAIR	Black, Navy Blue, Chocolate Brown	Yellow, Red, Gold, Orange, White	Lime Green, Kelly Green, Baby Blue	Bright Red, White, Red-Orange, Purple, Fuchsia

Source: The **Shape** magazine Fashion Editors.

Figure 12-1: Posing Suit Color Chart.

FEMALE FACTORS

Relatively few serious women bodybuilders use birth control pills, since the hormones in the pill can cause considerable water retention. Preferred alternatives for sexually active women are condoms (for male partners), diaphragms, and IUDs.

Water retention caused by a woman bodybuilder's menstrual cycle can also be a problem when a competition has been scheduled, although many women have competed successfully during peak water retention periods. And most women bodybuilders tend to hold much less water when they have been training hard and dieting. If menstrual water retention is a significant problem for you, your best course of action is to choose competitions synchronized for times when you have no problem with water retention.

GO FOR IT!

Bodybuilding is a sport of self-determination—you win and lose entirely on your own merits. Do you want to be a winner? Then get into the gym and start putting some of the advice contained in this book into practice. Go for it!

INDEX

A

Abdomen, 26
Abdominal board, 141, 143
Advanced bodybuilder, 13
Aerobics, 177
AFWB, 164
AFWB/IFBB, 185. *See also* IFBB
Alcohol, 168
Alternate Dumbbell Curls, 115
American Champion, 23, 178
American Women's Bodybuilding
    Champion, 15, 111
Anatomy
    abdominal, 140
    arm, 112
    back, 54
    calf, 42
    chest, 74
    hip, 24
    shoulder, 93–94
    thigh, 24
Appetite, 156
Arms, 111–37

B

Balanchine, George, 190
Bar twists, 140, 149–50
Barbell Bent Rows, 62, 63, 162, 179
Barbell Concentration Curls, 121, 162,
    179

Barbell Curls, 12, 13, 14, 17, 113–14
Barbell Preacher Curls, 20
Barbell Presses, 96, 97
Barbell Rows, 54, 112, 159
Barbell Toe Raises, 42–43, 44
Barbell Wrist Curls, 133
Basile, Debbie, 139, 167
Baxter, Kay, 41, 111, 162
Beals, Jennifer, 188
Benches, 16
    decline, 74
    flat exercise, 74
    45-degree angle, 162
    hyperextension, 60
    incline, 74, 76
    preacher, 21
    30-degree incline, 162
Bench Leg Raises, 143
Bench Presses, 13, 14, 74–75, 76, 77,
    112, 159
Bench Squats, 26
Bent Arm Pullovers, 54, 89
Bent Laterals, 162
Bent Twists, 150
Bentley, Stacey, 160
Beverly Hills, Diet, 191
Biofeedback, 156
Birth control, 192
Bowen, Lori, 23, 41, 178
Breathing, 165
Burn reps, 14
Burns, 12, 14
Burns, slow, 16

C

Cable Bent Laterals, 106
Cable Crossovers, 10, 87
Cable Curls, 119
Cable Flyes, 84
Cable Leg/Hip Movements, 36–37
Cable Reverse Curls, 130
Cable Side Laterals, 103
Caesar's Palace Pro Invitational, 23, 185
Calf Presses, 18, 46
Calories, 167, 168, 169
Cellulite, 14
Cheating, 12, 13
Cheating Reps, 14, 21
Cheshire, Carolyn, 139
Chest, 73–91
Chins, 54, 66, 162
Chins behind Neck, 66
Close-Grip Bench Presses, 123
Combes, Laura, 15, 73, 111, 139
Competition, 181–92
Compound Sets, 18–19
Conkwright, Lynn, 23, 111
Cross-Bench Dumbbell Pullovers, 54
Cross-Bench Pullover, 89
Crunches, 140, 147, 164
Csencsits, Candy, 4, 17, 175
Curl-Up, 141
Cuts, frontal thigh, 31

D

Deadlifts, 59
Decline Flyes, 83
Decline Presses, 77, 78, 81
Delts. *See* Muscles, deltoids
Descending Sets, 12, 21
Diana, Deborah, 14, 111, 157
Diet, 1, 53, 139, 167–73
    precontest, 171
    weight-gain, 169–70
    weight-loss, 170
Dips between Benches, 129
Distress, 158
Donkey Toe Raises, 47
Double-Biceps Shots, 111
Drugs, 164–65
    thyroid, 164
Dumbbell Bench Presses, 78, 83
Dumbbell Bent Laterals, 105, 106
Dumbbell Bent Rows, 63
Dumbbell Concentration Curls, 120,
    162, 179, 180
Dumbbell Curls, 114–15
Dumbbell Flyes, 74, 83, 84
Dumbbell Kickbacks, 128, 162
Dumbbell Presses, 97
Dumbbell Rows, 54, 112

Dumbbell Shrugs, 57
Dumbbell Side Laterals, 101
Dumbbell Triceps Extensions, 124
Dumbbell Wrist Curls, 133
Dunlap, Carla, 3, 4, 23, 53, 73, 111, 139,
    185–90
Dyederm, 191

E–F

Elliot-Kolakowski, Lisa, 39, 161
Elomaa, Kike, 12
Energetics, 41
Eustress, 158
Exercises, 7. *See also* specific exercise
    names
    abdominal, 140–53
    arm, 113–37
    back, 10, 55–71
    calf, 42–51
    chest, 74–91
    hip, 24
    isolation, 159
    shoulder, 94–109
    thigh, 24
Failure, 15
Fatigue, 10, 16, 20, 159
Fatigue pain, 9
Fatigue toxins, 9, 14, 53, 180
Fats, 170
Film work, 5
Flashdance, 188
Flat Bench, 143, 146
Flat Bench Cable Flyes, 87
Flat Bench Flyes, 83
Flex, 4, 181
Food supplements, 4
Forced Negatives, 17
Forced Reps, 12, 21
Forward Leg Kick, 37
Francis, Bev, 53, 73, 111, 139
Free-posing program, 23
Frog Kicks, 144
Front Chins, 66
Front Lat Pulldowns, 67, 164
Front Raises, 100, 162
Front Squats, 26–27
Frost-Larsen, Lisser, 139

G–H

Giant sets, 18–19, 21
Glass, Chris, 139, 164
Glutes. *See* Muscles, gluteus maximus
Gluteus maximus. *See* Muscles, gluteus
    maxiums
Goals, 1
Gold's Classic Champion, 111, 161, 162
Gold's Gym, 156

Good Mornings, 61
Grooming, 190
Gruwell, Shelley, 4, 18, 185
Hack Squats, 29
Hacks. *See* Hack Squats
Half Squats, 26
Hanging Leg Raises, 144, 164
High-resistance body, 24
Hyperextensions, 60
Hypertrophy, 11

I–K

IFBB. *See* International Federation of
    Bodybuilders
IFBB World Champions, 156
Incline Bench Presses, 78
Incline Dumbbell Curls, 115–16
Incline Dumbbell Presses, 162
Incline Flyes, 83
Incline Presses, 10, 16, 76, 77
Income, 3
Insomnia, 156
International Federation of
    Bodybuilders, 164, 182
Isolation movemnt, 20
Judges, 182, 185
Joint injuries, 16
Junk foods, 168
Kinesiology
    abdominal, 140
    arm, 112
    back, 54
    calf, 42
    chest, 74
    hip, 24
    shoulder, 93–94
    thigh, 24
Knee-Ups, 146

L

L Crunches, 147
Lat Machine Pulldown, 54, 67–68, 162
Lat Thickness, 54
Lat Width, 54
Lateral Raises, 179
Lats. *See* Muscles, latissimus dorsi
Leather weightlifting belt, 26
Leg Abduction, 36
Leg Adduction, 36
Leg Curls, 32, 34, 59, 162
Leg Extensions, 32, 33, 162
Leg Presses, 24, 27–28
Leg Raises, 140, 141, 143
Legs, 23–39
Lipotropics, 169
Low-intensity aerobics, 24
Lunges, 30

Lying Barbell Triceps Extensions, 122,
    123
Lying Dumbbell Curls, 115
Lying Leg Curls, 33
Lyon, Lisa, 5

M

Machine Curls, 179
Machine Shrugs, 57
Machines, exercise, 10, 14, 17
    back, 29
    calf, 15, 44
    45-degree, 28, 46
    leg, 32
    leg extension, 47
    leg press, 18
    Nautilus, 28, 33, 46, 127
    seated calf, 45
    standing calf, 42–43
    Universal, 28, 57
    Universal Gym leg press, 46
    yoke-type, 29
McLish, Rachel, 23, 24, 111, 139, 142,
    185
McNew, Julie, 111
Menstrual cycle, 192
Miss Olympia, 17, 23, 24, 111, 175, 185
Muscle & Fitness, 4, 16, 185
Muscle detail, 17
Muscle development, 17
Muscle endurance, 16
Muscle injuries, 16
Muscle mass, 9, 10, 12, 16, 17, 23, 169
Muscle power, 16
Muscle quality, 9, 12
Muscle strength, 12, 16, 17, 169
Muscle tone, 12
Muscles
    abdominal, 139–53, 176
    anterior deltoid, 107, 123
    back, 19, 176
    biceps, 12, 13, 18, 20, 21, 107, 112,
        113, 114–15, 116, 118, 119, 120,
        121, 130, 179, 180
    biceps femoris, 24, 34
    buttocks, 23, 25, 29, 30
    brachialis, 107, 112, 130
    calves, 176
    chest, 19, 176
    deltoids, 14
    forearm, 107, 112, 118
    forearm extensors, 18, 112, 118
    forearm flexors, 18, 112, 113, 114, 115,
        116, 119, 133, 134
    gluteus maximus, 24
    hamstring, 18, 27, 29, 33, 34
    hip, 23
    hip girdle, 24

inner triceps, 124
intercostal, 140, 142, 144
leg, 25
leg abductors, 24
leg adductors, 24
lower back, 26
medial deltoids, 107
medial triceps, 124
obliques, 140
pectorals, 18, 123
posterior deltoids, 107
quadriceps, 19, 24, 28, 29, 31, 32
rectus abdominis, 140, 141, 142, 143,
    144
shoulders, 176
supinators, 112, 130
thigh, 19, 23, 24, 176
thigh adductors, 25
trapezius, 25, 107
triceps, 18, 20, 112, 122, 123, 124, 125,
    126, 127, 128, 129, 180
upper back, 106
upper hamstrings, 30

N–O

Narrow-Grip Benches, 123
Nautilus Bench Presses, 80
Nautilus Curls, 118
Nautilus Flyes, 80, 86
Nautilus Pullovers, 54, 68
Nautilus Side Laterals, 102
Nautilus Triceps Extensions, 127, 128
Negative Reps. *See* Weider Principles,
    retrogravity
Nutrition Almanac, 171
Nutrition, 7, 167
Oiling, 191
One-Arm Cable Curls, 119
One-Arm Dumbbell Bent Rows, 164
One-Leg Calf Raises, 162, 179
One-Leg Toe Raises, 43, 48
Off-season cycle, 10
Overhead Presses, 112
Overtraining 17, 112

P

Pain barrier, 9
Parallel Bar Dips, 81, 112, 144
Parallel Bars, 144
Parallel Squats, 26
Partial reps. *See* Burns
Partial Squats, 26
Past failure, 21
Peak Contraction, 127, 147
Pec Deck Flyes, 10, 74, 85, 86, 162
Pecs. *See* Muscles, pectorals
Personal appearances, 4

Personal coaching, 4
Photos, 4
Physiologists, 17
Plakinger, Tina, 53
Point of failure, 16, 21
Poses
    double-biceps, 187, 188
    leg stance, 187
    side chest, 187
    side triceps, 188
Posing, 177, 180, 182, 185–90
    body attitude, 186
    compulsory, 187–88
    exhibitions, 3
    free, 188
    personal appearances, 190
    suits, 4, 190–91
Post-warm-up set, 12
Preacher Curls, 116–17
Preexhaustion Supersets, 19, 21
Presses behind Neck, 96
Prize money, 1, 3
Pro World Champion, 12, 23, 41, 111,
    185
Product endorsements, 4
Professional bodybuilding, 3–7
Progression
    advanced, 10–11
    resistance, 9–11
Protein, 169, 170, 172–73
    efficiency ration, 172
    supplements, 171
Pulldowns behind Neck, 67
Pulley Extensions behind Head, 126
Pulley Preacher Curls, 117
Pulley Pushdowns, 125
Pulley Rows, 112, 162
Pullovers, 68
Pulse rate, 156
Pushdowns, 126
Pyramid system
    definition, 10
    descending, 10

Q–R

Quads. *See* Muscles, quadriceps
Quality training, 10
Quarter Squats, 26
Rear Leg Kick, 37
Rest interval, 18
Rest-Pause workouts, 21
Rest time, 16
Reverse Curls, 112, 130
Reynolds, Bill, 158
Roman Chair Sit-Ups, 142
Rope Crunches, 140, 149
Rotating Shoulder Shrugs, 57
Routines

abdominal, 152–53
arm, 135–37
back, 70–71
calf, 49–51
chest, 90–91
hip, 38
individual, 158–59
leg, 38
shoulder, 108–9
split and double-split, 160–61
thigh, 38
Rules, AFWB/IFWB, 181

S

Salt, 168
Seated Barbell Presses, 95
Seated Calf Raises, 188
Seated Dumbbell Curls, 115
Seated Pulley Rows, 10, 54, 64, 164
Seated Toe Raises, 42
Self-discipline, 2
Self-esteem, 3
Self-reliance, 2
Selye, Dr. Hans, 158
Shape, 4
Shoulder Shrugs, 56–57
Shoulders, 93–109
Side Bends, 140, 150
Side Laterals, 101, 162
Sissy Squats, 31
Sit-Ups, 140–41, 142
Skin tone, 190
Snacks, 170
Sports conditioning, 24
Squats, 14, 23, 24, 25–26, 27, 30, 42, 159
Standing Barbell Curls, 162
Standing Barbell Presses, 94–95, 96
Standing Barbell Wrist Curls, 134
Standing Calf Machine Raises, 49
Standing Calf Raises, 15
Standing Dumbbell Presses, 14
Standing Leg Curls, 33, 34
Standing Toe Raises, 42
Steroids, anabolic, 164
Sticking point, 13
Stiff-Arm Pulldowns, 164
Stiff-Arm Pullovers, 54, 88, 89
Stiff-Leg Deadlifts, 35, 59–60
Stimulants, energy, 164
Stress, 13
management, 158
negative. *See* Distress
positive. *See* Eustress
reducing, 158
Stretching, post-workout, 158
Strength levels, 10
Strength potentials, 10
Sugar, 168

Supersets, 18–19, 21
Swedish Champion, 13

T

T-Bar Rows, 65
T-Shirts, 4
Tanning, 177, 190
Torso muscle groups, 20
Training
advanced, 155–65
equipment, 4
flexibility, 158
instinct, 155–57
intensity, 7, 9
partners, 12, 14, 16, 67
quality, 178
routines, 7
seminars, 4
Training past failure, 12
Training secrets, 142
abdominal, 140
arms, 112
back, 54
calf, 42
chest, 74
hip, 24
shoulder, 94
thigh, 24
Training to failure, 11–12, 13
Transition periods, 177
Traps. *See* Muscles, trapezius
Twisting Crunches, 140
Twisting Leg Raises, 144
Twisting Roman Chair Sit-Ups, 142
Twisting Sit-Ups, 140
Trisets, 18–19, 21

U–W

Upright Rows, 55–56, 107, 179
USA Champion, 111, 178
USA Couples Champion, 111
Variable removal, 14
Visualization, 165
Vitamins, 169, 171
Warm-downs, 158
Warm-ups, 16, 158
Water, 169, 173
retention, 192
Weider Book of Bodybuilding, 1, 3
Weider, Joe, 180
Weider Good Life Multipaks, 169
Weider Research Clinic, 158, 164
Weider Principles, 12
cheating, 13, 14, 177
confusion training, 42
cycle training, 175–78
descending sets, 14, 177

holistic sets, 159
double-split system, 161
forced reps, 13–14, 177
instinctive training, 13, 156, 168, 172
intensification training, 162
isotension, 177, 180–81
muscle confusion, 162
muscle priority, 159, 177
peak contraction, 85, 162–63, 177,
    178–79
preexhaustion, 20
quality training, 10, 178
rest–pause, 16–17
retro-gravity, 12, 14, 16, 17–18, 21, 80

slow, continuous tension, 164, 177,
    179–80
staggered sets, 164
Weider System of Bodybuilding, 7
Workouts, 9–21
World Champion, 13, 23, 156, 168, 185
World Grand Prix Champion, 18

X–Z

Your Physique, 16
Zane Pro Invitational, 160
Zetterqvist, Inger, 13, 23, 139, 156